Appreciating and Collecting Historical Technology

COLLECTING TECH

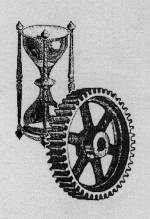

ISBN: 978-1-931626-30-9

Published by
Astragal Press
An Imprint of Finney Company
8075 215th Street West
Lakeville, Minnesota 55044
www.finneyco.com
www.astragalpress.com

Printed in the United States of America
1 3 5 7 9 10 8 6 4 2

Invention, Engineering and Science

COLLECTING TECH

A collection of objects, antique and historical, compiled
with diverse and curious observations about their:

Use

History

Social Context

Design

Beauty

Value

Peter F. Stone

ACKNOWLEDGMENTS

No technology has replaced a knowledgeable human in correcting errors of fact, concept and taste in preparing a book for publication. My friends have done their best to protect this work (and me) from these errors. I am deeply indebted to them for their kindness and generosity in suggesting corrections and improvements. Surviving errors are my sole responsibility.

Donald Arnstine made many thoughtful and valuable suggestions as an interested initiate in technology. Mathew Baylen provided his insights as an electrical engineer. The contributions of Richard Sommerfeld from a scientific standpoint are deeply appreciated. I am indebted to David Baylen and Robbii Wessen for their hard work in adapting my stone age computer files to the 20th century. I thank Robert Nesbit for his suggestions and corrections. Lieutenant Colonel Jack L. Miller, U.S.A.F., kindly assisted with information relating to radio navigation. The librarians at the Buchanan Public Library, Buchanan, Michigan, helped me with my research and I thank them. Scott Weinstein has my gratitude for his contribution of a digital camera to this project. Donna Dunlap and Bob Lance offered encouragement when it was needed. Michael Studier shares my enthusiasm for historical technology and brings to that enthusiasm the discipline of an industrial engineer. In his review of this work, he made substantial corrections. Julia Studier undertook a much-needed copy editing of the text and left it greatly improved. I am deeply grateful to Michael and Julia for their help.

With affection, this book is dedicated to Valerie Janet Ohlhausen.

CONTENTS

Introduction   3

1 Promoting Domestic Tranquility   5

2 At Sea   25

3 Mighty in Strength and Endurance   49

4 Franklin's Folly   65

5 Awarding the Daedalus   85

6 Frontiers of Knowledge   105

7 Measuring the Land   121

8 The Tool-Using Animal   141

9 On the Job   159

10 Collecting   181

     Historical Technology as Art   182

     Acquisition   183

     Valuation   185

     Research   187

     Dating Historical Technology   189

     Fakes, Forgeries and Reproductions   192

     Cleaning, Conservation and Restoration   195

     About Technology   198

Antique Technology Collectors Associations   202

Glossary   203

Bibliography   205

Graphics Credits   206

Index   207

As machines, or artefacts, become obsolete they are usually destroyed. They are old, out of date, superseded, not worth keeping. Slowly, as the years pass, they become more and more interesting; valuable, even, until, when there are few left, they become precious relics.

– Donald Cardwell

INTRODUCTION

Why is historical technology fascinating? For every piece of historical technology, there are strings attached. Pull one of these strings and you'll find a story. A tragedy or triumph for the inventor, a drama of social turmoil, a scientific mystery solved, an anecdote or historical vignette — all these strings ultimately woven into the fabric of our contemporary technology. You can hold the evidence in your hand, feel it and examine it. This evidence, this bit of technology has other attractions.

Many objects of historical technology are beautiful. They evolved from need uncorrupted by fashion or schools of decoration. They address their purpose simply, directly, unencumbered by ornament. This is the aesthetic of function. This aesthetic is often more comfortable and natural than the self-conscious design of many contemporary products. In the best of historical technology, we see a synthesis of creative problem-solving, social benefit and artistry.

The materials and manufacturing processes of items of historical technology add to their interest. Production was expensive so materials were carefully chosen. These materials were, on balance, more costly and durable than those used today. Planned obsolescence was unknown. The fingerprints of manufacturing — lathe marks, casting marks, sawtooth gouges, forge hammer blows are still there to be read. These traces of manufacturing processes add character. They have nothing to do with the anonymity of plastic.

Objects of historical technology document our technical development. The tarnish on that old brass sextant is evidence of both neglect and technological progress. The hours spent finding latitude and longitude with a sextant have been shortened to an instant through global positioning satellites. The U.S. Naval Academy stopped teaching celestial navigation in 1998.

A slide rule, a steam engine, and an antique plane are treasures. These old objects merit our collection and preservation. Their signs of wear and breakage tell us how they were actually used. These same signs speak to us from the past of close human association. They are mementos of a time when technology was easier to understand and a time when the individual personalities of inventors, engineers, scientists, and manufacturers left a larger and more dramatic impression.

For these reasons and more, we appreciate and enjoy objects of historical technology. We're fortunate we can collect and possess them.

We should expand our notion of what is important and collectible. Not just scientific or engineering instruments and hand tools, but machine tools, engines and significant parts, dies, molds, cutters and gears. These document our history, as well. Collecting the unusual and obscure has its special rewards. You will learn more about technology, experience the joy of discovery and your collection will cost less to acquire. Its value is likely to grow more rapidly as interest in historical technology increases. Another advantage: such collecting is practical.

Nineteenth-century and early 20th-century technology is still available. Most of the objects in this book date from this period. Objects from earlier periods are rarely available outside of expensive antiques stores and major auctions. So, the kinds of objects in this collection bought at flea markets, antiques malls, garage sales and local auctions represent a reasonable goal for the current collector.

In this book we look backwards, but we do so with pleasure and pride in the evidence of our technological accomplishments. If you are curious about technology and the objects that reveal its history and artistry, you should enjoy the following collection and commentary.

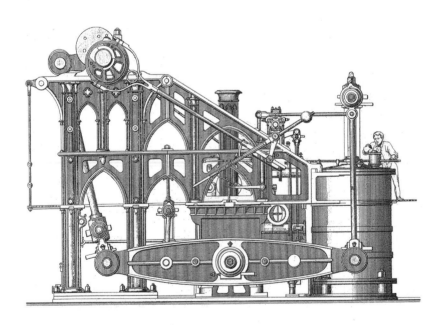

1 PROMOTING DOMESTIC TRANQUILITY

Coffee grinder
Sad iron
Duck press
Clock
Wheel barometer
Sewing machine
Spinning wheel
Apple parer
Binoculars
Lock
Player harmonica
Pocket watch
Copper tea kettle
Wallpaper printing cylinder
Rifle

What promotes domestic tranquility? Let's set aside such imponderables as love, trust, security and reality TV. We'll focus on things. Many things are sold with the promise of improving domestic life and most betray that promise. A few things described in this section have fulfilled the promise at one time or another. They have eased the burden of domestic chores, but these are still onerous despite all our appliances. As Joan Rivers said, "I hate housework! You make the beds, you do the dishes – and six months later you have to start all over again."

The goal of making domestic life easy, comfortable and pleasant has surely inspired more devices, gadgets and mechanisms than any other endeavor. The pages of mail order catalogs show that this goal still challenges our ingenuity. Most of the devices in this section developed through incremental improvements with time-tested usefulness. Though some have fossilized in the basement or attic, many are extant in our parlors, kitchens and laundries.

Imagine the evolutionary line of toasters climbing from the primordial ooze and morphing from stove top to electrical to microwave to computerized models. Looking into the future, we can see its continued evolution. The toaster cuts off the crust, if you like, and then butters your toast, as well. If computerized, it might personalize your toast by branding it with the most important events of your day. Of course, it includes a clock/radio. As these devices evolve, we can expect many dysfunctional mutations, but a few will still have survival benefit.

Domestic Technology Time Line

Approximate Year of Manufacture of Objects in this Chapter		Year of Significant Events
	1657	Huygens invents pendulum clock
	1679	Pressure cooker invented
	1804	Food canning process invented
Wheel barometer	1840	Iron apple parer invented
	1841	Wooden sewing machine invented
Tea kettle	1850	
Spinning wheel	1860	Henry invents lever action rifle
	1876	Phonograph invented
	1884	Fountain pen invented
	1891	Zipper invented
Rifle	1894	
Sewing machine	1900	Paper clip invented
	1902	Air conditioning invented
Pocket watch	1908	Electric vacuum cleaner invented
	1909	Electric toaster invented
Clock	1910	
Wallpaper printing cylinder	1910	
Coffee grinder	1910	
Apple parer	1916	
	1918	Electric food mixer invented
	1919	Frigidaire refrigerator introduced
Duck press	1920	First commercial radio broadcast
Player harmonica	1920	
Binoculars	1925	
	1927	Pop up toaster invented
Sad iron	1929	Color television invented
	1929	Frozen food introduced
	1932	Home dishwasher invented
	1938	Ballpoint pen invented
	1944	Tupperware introduced

Coffee Grinder

Originating in Abyssinia, the use of coffee spread throughout the Arab world in about 1470. The first European coffee house was established in London in 1652. Some thought that coffee beans were the seeds of revolution. In 1675, Charles II of England tried to suppress coffee houses. His royal proclamation stated that they were the resort of disaffected persons "who devised and spread abroad diverse false, malicious, and scandalous reports, to the defamation of His Majesty's Government and to the disturbance of the peace and quiet of the nation." What plots, do you suppose, are brewing at Starbucks?

Coffee grinders are a sought-after subset of kitchen collectibles. There is a huge variety of designs and mechanical arrangements. In America, one of the most popular was the Arcade Crystal coffee grinder.

Founded in 1868 as the Novelty Iron Works, the company became Arcade Manufacturing when it moved to Freeport, Illinois, in 1885. The company was bought by Rockwell Manufacturing in 1946. Originally, the company produced farming equipment and then increased its line to toys and other cast iron items. Its first coffee grinders were the conventional wooden boxes with a crank on top and a drawer. Then, in about 1905, they designed the cast iron wall mounted grinder with a glass hopper on top to hold the coffee beans. The wing nut and locking thumbwheel at the base of the handle adjust the fineness of the grind. Because of their heavy-duty construction, most of the surviving grinders are still operable.

The grinder top left is Arcade Crystal No. 3, with ornate Victorian cast floral relief. Height: 19 in. Top right is the same grinder in a copper plated version. The second grinder on the right is a less ornate and basic version. The grinder on the bottom right is Arcade Crystal No. 4, made up of flat planes with an Art Deco aspect.

Some rugged individualist said, "There is no such thing as strong coffee, only weak people." Abraham Lincoln, with a more refined palate, said, "If this is coffee, please bring me some tea; but if this is tea, please bring me some coffee."

Arcade Crystal No. 3 coffee grinder - same type, quality and period - 2003 - $160

Sad Iron

This is a Monitor sad iron. John C. Lake founded the Monitor Sad Iron Company. He named the company after the Union ironclad warship, *Monitor.* We don't know whether he did this out of Union sympathies or because he thought the sad iron looked like the *Monitor.*

We are fairly certain, however, that the Flatiron Building in Times Square was so named because its triangular shape resembled a flatiron.

Since Monday was wash day, Tuesday was ironing day and a sad iron was heated up. A sad iron is "sad" in archaic usage for heavy or weighty. A sad ironer's lot is not a happy one. Ironing with a sad iron or flatiron, weighing between 5 to 9 pounds, was hot, hard work. When the iron was heated by an internal torch, the work was also risky. Alcohol fuels this sad iron. Other sad irons were fueled with kerosene or gasoline. These irons sometimes caught fire and even exploded. Burns on fingers and hands were common, evidence supporting Erma Bombeck's statement, "Housework, if done right, can kill you."

This sad iron is nickel plated brass and iron with wooden handle. Based on its latest patent number, 1712004, it was made about 1929. A brass plate under the handle reads:

> Model C   MONITOR
> Made in the U.S.A. by
> The Monitor Sad Iron Co.
> Big Prairie, Ohio

Length: 7 1/4 in. Width: 3 5/8 in. Height at fuel can: 6 3/4 in.

Sad iron - same type, quality and period - 2004 - $25

Duck Press

This invention of the French, *presse à canard*, has the sole purpose of extracting juices from the carcass of a duck. Another accessory that no kitchen should be without. In the following recipe, a mallard is preferable to a base canard.

Executive Summary of Pressed Duck Recipe

Take Donald or Daffy and partially roast (20 minutes). Remove legs and slice off breast meat. Complete roasting of legs and set aside. Place remaining carcass in duck press and extract juices. Mix juices with reduced wine or port and cognac. Place in chaffing dish with breast meat and heat *below* the boiling point. Serve breast meat and legs. Even shorter version: chuck the duck and drink the wine and cognac.

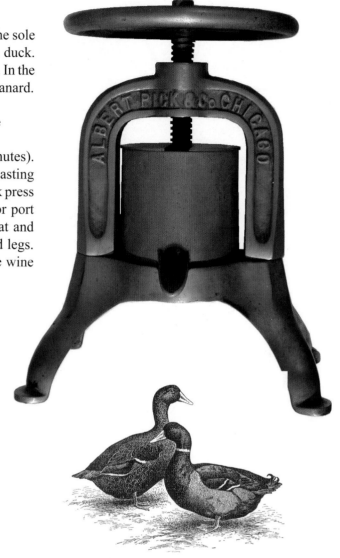

A Rouen restaurateur named Mèchenet invented the recipe at the beginning of the 19th century. The dish became the house specialty of La Tour D'Argent in Paris in 1890. The owner, Frederic Delair, began a duck census, numbering and recording each and every pressed duck served by the restaurant. Here are a few of the notables served and the serial numbers of their ducks.

Edward VII, the Prince of Wales	# 328
Theodore Roosevelt	# 33,642
Charlie Chaplin	# 253,652
Emperor Hiro Hito	# 423,900
Mayor Rudy Giuliani	# 971,612

Some duck presses have extremely ornate frames cast as floral ropes or dolphins and some have been made of solid silver. Though not as useless as a dodo press, a duck press of solid silver surely qualifies as conspicuous consumption. This industrial-strength duck press of the early 20th century weighs in at 40 pounds. It is nickel-plated iron. The internal strainer is silver-plated brass.

Cast raised lettering on frame: ALBERT PICK & Co CHICAGO

Height screwed down: 16 1/2 in. Width at base: 14 in. Depth at base: 8 in. Handwheel diameter: 10 1/2 in.

Albert Pick & Co. originally manufactured and distributed hotel and restaurant kitchen equipment and later developed into a hotel chain.

Contemporary duck presses are priced from $1,500 to $2,000. This is a bit high considering their simple technology. It seems the device is designed to press the duck and the price is designed to soak the epicure.

Clock

Here's the difference between you and Galileo. When you're sitting in church and bored with the same old hell fire and damnation sermon, you think about football, mortgage payments or supper. When Galileo was sitting in the church of Florence and was bored with the same old hell fire and damnation sermon, he noticed the swaying chandelier above his head. "Strange," he thought, "the chandelier takes the same amount of time to swing whether the arcs are short or long." The phenomenon is isochronism. This led him to design a pendulum clock. The clock was never built. In 1657, Christian Huygens mathematically demonstrated isochronism for short arcs, patented the pendulum escapement and built the first working pendulum clock.

Overall diameter including the oak frame: 14 1/2 in.

No makers' marks.

Christian Huygens

This is a simple, but well-made English clock of the late nineteenth century. It was probably used in a post office or railway station. It has a spring-powered pendulum movement. Here, you see a part of the movement. The large drum or barrel contains the spring. A gut cable connects this barrel to the fusee. A fusee averages the strength of the mainspring as it unwinds. As the spring uncoils and its tension weakens, the fusee increases the spring's mechanical advantage, providing a more constant impulse to the pendulum. The fusee itself is the spirally grooved cone in the center. Leonardo da Vinci's sketchbook of about 1485 illustrates a fusee and its invention may be attributed to him. As special alloys used in springs improved so that they provided constant pressure, the fusee became obsolete.

Even though they possessed the standard number of fingers, the Summerians of 6,000 BC used a numeric system to the base 60. So, out of respect, habit or lack of originality, we have 60 seconds in a minute, 60 minutes in an hour, and 360 degrees in a circle. Here's how we measure the fourth dimension: the mean solar second is the primary standard of time, one eighty six thousand four hundredth part of a mean solar day. The longest period of time: the age of the universe is about 14 billion years (a sum dwarfed by the national debt). The shortest measured period of time: the decay of an elementary particle is 0.0000000000000000000001 second. The shortest unit of time measurements is used in nuclear physics. It is one "shake" or 10^{-8} seconds, facetiously named after the shake of a lamb's tail.

Einstein tells us that, as we approach the speed of light, mass increases and time slows. These results are unfortunate. Increasing mass adds to the epidemic of obesity and retarding time induces boredom.

See "Watch."

Fusee wall clock - same type, quality and period - 2004 - $875

Wheel Barometer

A barometer measures changes in atmospheric pressure as an aid to weather forecasting. A key component is a vacuum.

There are vacuous observations about vacuums. Galileo, Rabelais and Spinoza all opined that nature abhors a vacuum. In reality, nature *loves* a vacuum. The estimated average density of matter in the universe is 9.9×10^{-30} grams per cubic centimeter. An almost infinitesimal density. The rest of the universe is a vacuum, an almost infinite volume.

"Often mistaken, but never uncertain" characterizes the scientific observations of Aristotle. Among them, he states that, "a vacuum cannot exist." Because of this prevalent belief, the barometer was not truly understood, even after its invention. In fact, a nearly perfect vacuum forms at the top of the column in a mercury barometer.

Evangelista Torricelli invented the first mercury barometer in 1643. In 1665, Robert Hooke created the first wheel barometer. Here is how the wheel barometer works.

Air pressure acts on the weight floating on the mercury in the glass tube. This pressure moves the weight and counterweight suspended from the pulley wheel, rotating the pulley. The pulley is attached to the dial hand which registers the pressure.

The alcohol thermometer with engraved silvered face reads from 0 to 110 degrees Fahrenheit with indications for extremely cold, freezing, temperate, summer heat, blood heat, fever heat. The engraved silvered barometer dial reads from 28 to 31 inches with indications for stormy, much rain, rain, change, fair, set fair, very dry.

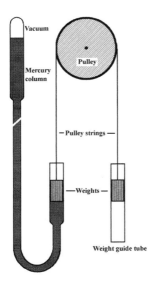

The case is mahogany inlaid with flowers and stars with striped boxwood and ebony stringing. Made about 1840. The style is Georgian. Height: 38 1/2 in. Diameter of face: 10 1/2 in. Depth at face: 3 in.

As the sole predictor of weather, barometric pressure is not very reliable. Additional input of wind speed and direction, temperature, and humidity for computerized weather models reduces the frequency of apologies from your local forecaster.

"Satellite photography in the 1970s gave rise to the long-range weather forecast, a month at a time. This in turn gave rise to the observation that the long-range weather forecast was wrong most of the time. In turn, this gave rise to the dropping of the long-range weather forecast, and to the admission that really accurate forecasting could only cover the next day or two, and not always then." Miles Kingston

No other weather forecast has achieved the reliability of George Carlin's forecast for tonight: "dark."

See "Barograph."   Wheel barometer - same type, quality and period - 2003 - $1,200

Paris, 1841, the Luddites shout, "A mort!" They chase the tailor from his shop. The uniforms he made for the French Army go up in smoke. And with them, the first practical sewing machines. These were the tailor's invention and the objects of mob fear and fury. Barthelemy Thimonier fled for his life. His invention brought him nothing but grief. In 1857, Thimonier died without a sou. Others reaped the profits. The inventive improvements of Elias Howe made him a millionaire through patent royalties. As the premier sewing machine manufacturer, Isaac Merritt Singer also became a millionaire. He was inventive and procreative. Singer had 20 patents and 24 children.

From SCIENTIFIC AMERICAN, 1854

Sewing Machine.

About five years ago we do not believe there were over three or four sewing machines in use in our country, now they can be counted by thousands. They are found in the factories and in private dwellings, sewing the coarse bag and the most delicate piece of cambric.— These machines, since they were first introduced, have advanced towards perfection with a rapidity that is truly astonishiug. So many patents have already been obtained for improvements that it is very difficult to keep posted up in their progress; this is evidence of their importance, and at the same time, it is a sign that applications of them for various purposes, demands new modifications, devices and arrangements.

Sewing Machine

The design of this sewing machine copies that of a Willcox & Gibbs machine of about 1890. James Gibbs pioneered the manufacture and marketing of cheaper sewing machines in about 1857. At that time his sewing machine cost $50, while other machines cost twice as much. Singer was his competitor.

Black enameled cast iron frame with flowery ornamentation in gold. Nickel-plated platform and wheel.

Length: 10 in. Height: 9 in. Width: 6 in.

On the base: B. ELDREDGE AUTOMATIC

                          MANUFACTURED BY
On the platform: NATIONAL SEWING MACHINE COMPANY
                    BELVEDERE ILL & NEW YORK

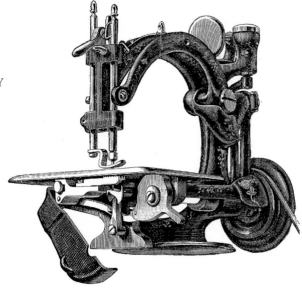

Sewing machines - same type, quality and period -
1986 - $40
1998 - $130

Spinning Wheel

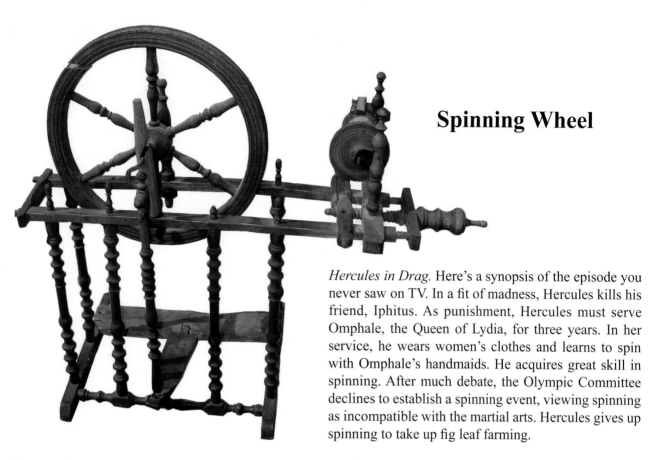

Hercules in Drag. Here's a synopsis of the episode you never saw on TV. In a fit of madness, Hercules kills his friend, Iphitus. As punishment, Hercules must serve Omphale, the Queen of Lydia, for three years. In her service, he wears women's clothes and learns to spin with Omphale's handmaids. He acquires great skill in spinning. After much debate, the Olympic Committee declines to establish a spinning event, viewing spinning as incompatible with the martial arts. Hercules gives up spinning to take up fig leaf farming.

If Hercules used a spinning wheel, he would have used a cotton or wool wheel and not a flax wheel, such as this one. What's the difference? Cotton has relatively short fibers, about 1/2 to 2 inches in length. Wool is variable in length up to 20 in. Flax is up to 36 in. in length. Short fiber lengths require faster twisting rates. A larger wheel permits faster twisting rates. So, a small wheel would be used for flax.

This form of spinning wheel is called a frame or Norwegian type. It has a single treadle. Note the ornamental spooling of the legs. Dates to about the mid-19th century. Height: 24 in. Length 27 in.

The spinning jenny and factory system began to supplant domestic spinning wheels towards the end of the 18th century. By the middle of the 19th century, factory-spun yarns were so cheap that the spinning wheel was practically obsolete. Spinning with the wheel continued, for awhile, as a fashionable drawing-room activity. To the left, you see an alternative use for some of those obsolete spinning wheels. Poor Hercules, lost in the mist of mythology, has no alternative use.

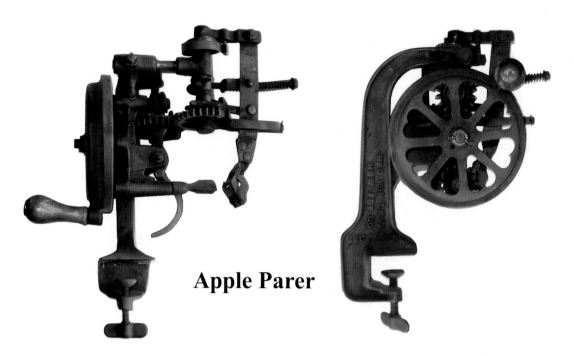

Apple Parer

If the fruit Eve gave to Adam was an apple, it would have been a crab apple. The crab apple is a small, sour and wild apple, a puny vessel for the knowledge of good and evil. Since the Bible is ambiguous, what was the forbidden fruit that Eve gave to Adam?

We'll consider several possibly tempting fruit according to three important criteria. These are appearance, storage and shipping qualities. Flavor is not a factor because fruit growers and distributors have deemed it irrelevant. As the name implies, passion fruit is a possibility, but it is unattractive and ships poorly. The pomegranate symbolizes fertility, but it, too, is homely in appearance though it does hold up well in shipment and storage. Grapes are attractive, ship and store well, and symbolize truth (*in vino veritas*), a plausible by-product of the tree of knowledge. Would Mother Eve have baked a grape pie? Doesn't sound quite right, but you be the judge.

The earliest apple parers were wood and made by the user. The U. S. Patent Office issued a great many apple parer patents. The first one went to Moses Coates in 1803. An iron apple parer was first patented in the 1840s. Because of the great variation of apple parers and the inventive originality of their designs, they have become a specialized area of antiques collecting. Some early models command a price of $600 and more.

IMPROVED APPLE PARING MACHINE

A good deal of mechanical engineering went into the design of this heavy duty cast iron apple parer. It sports two internal planetary gears, two intermittent gears, and a worm gear driving a mating gear. It is 13 in. high and 12 in. wide when the paring blade is at maximum extension. The brand is Buchi Success Parer, patented August 1, 1916. It was manufactured by the Chicago Hardware Foundry Company.

To the left is an apple parer from about 1865. It will pare and slice, but doesn't dice. No competition for Popeil.

It's as easy as apple pie. Not really! According to Carl Sagan, "If you want to make an apple pie from scratch, you must first create the universe."

14

Binoculars

These binoculars are aluminum and hard rubber. The two scopes focus independently.

First quarter of the 20th century

Markings on rear of prism chamber:

> Barr & Stroud
> 7 x CF 30
> Glasgow & London

Length: 9 1/8 in.
Diameter of objective lens bezel: 2 5/8 in.

In 1888, Archibald Barr was a professor of engineering and William Stroud was a professor of physics at Yorkshire College when they designed a military rangefinder. After some design improvements, the Admiralty adopted their rangefinder in 1892. They formed Barr & Stroud Ltd. in 1913. The company began manufacturing binoculars in 1919 and was awarded a contract to supply binoculars to the Royal Navy in 1930. The company was famed for its military optical equipment including rangefinders, gunsights, periscopes, telescopes and instruments for aerial and topographic survey.

Which of the following questions was first answered through the use of binoculars?

a. "Lieutenant, are those Indians or scouts on the top of that hill?"

b. "See the box in the third tier. Is Collete wearing a taffeta or satin gown?"

c. "That bird on the lowest branch, would you call it a painted bunting or a northern parula?"

d. "Captain, is that an iceberg dead ahead?"

Binoculars were introduced in about 1823 to French opera audiences as opera glasses. They derived from binocular telescopes, two linked telescopes. Binocular telescopes were used as early as 1720. In 1893, Ernst Abbé used prisms in binoculars to place objectives farther apart than oculars as in these binoculars. The prisms effectively lengthened the scope, permitting greater magnification in a shorter scope. They corrected the image vertically and enhanced the three dimensional aspect of the image.

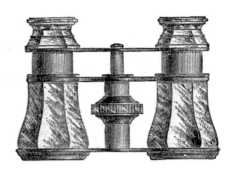

The power of binoculars is conventionally described by two numbers, thus: 7x30. The first number is the magnification, 7 times. The second number is the diameter of the objective lens in millimeters, 30 millimeters. For standard, hand-held binoculars, the magnification is limited to about 10 because of the natural vibration of the hands and the resulting vibration of the image. Typical opera glasses would have a power of 3x10, easily enough magnification to identify the fabric in Collete's gown and possibly sufficient to see the hickey on her neck.

See "Telescope."

Binoculars - same type, quality and period - 2003 - $225

Lock

In the mid-19th century, lock makers in America and England competed intensely for the invention of a pick-proof lock. The chief contender was an English tumbler lock invented by Joseph Bramah and subsequently improved. The manufacturer of this lock offered 200 guineas to anyone who could pick it. An American locksmith, A. G. Hobbs, picked up the challenge and picked at the lock for 30 days. He won the prize and, in turn, offered 200 guineas to anyone who could pick a lock of his own design. At the time, no one could do it.

Think of a key as a crank used to move a bolt back and forth. Assume that crank or key can only be turned in a lock hole because it has cutouts that match projections inside the lock. Those projections inside the lock that prevent non-matching keys from turning are termed "wards." Assume the key cannot be turned unless its edge aligns movable levers or pins to a precise position. These levers or pins are termed "tumblers."

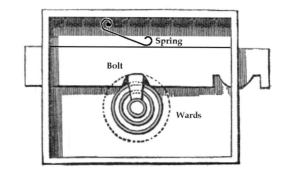

The oldest lock, an Egyptian lock from 4000 B.C., used tumblers, but no wards. Early locks, from ancient Greece and Rome, consisted of wards, but no tumblers. Since togas lacked pockets, the Romans made keys that could be worn as finger rings. Beginning in the late 18th century, locks used both wards and tumblers to prevent the wrong key from turning and moving the bolt.

This massive wrought iron lock is 13 in. by 9 1/2 in. It has only wards. Two springs hold a notch in the bolt against a projection. When the key is turned, it lifts the bolt so it can slide over the projection.

Where would a lock such as this be used? A castle gate? These were manned by guards. No need for a lock. A home? Unlikely, the key would be a burden. The hand-forged workmanship suggests some rural origin and usage. The most likely purpose: to lock a barn, granary or warehouse. We have not unlocked the mystery of its age and origin.

We want safety and security in our homes and workplaces. So, we purchase locks. Like the Maginot line or the Gordian knot, any security system can be breached by wit or brute force. If the security offered by locks is more seeming than substance, the illusion suffices for most of us.

Hand forged door lock - same type, quality and period - 2003 - $2,000

16

Player Harmonica and the Organ Grinder

From about 1850 in the United States, the organ grinder and his monkey were familiar denizens of the city streets. With an out-of-tune organ, the grinder could earn just as much with hush money as he could by playing. One might have to negotiate for peace and quiet. In which case, this negotiating principle applies: "Don't talk to the monkey when you can talk to the organ grinder." Such literati as Charles Dickens, Alfred Lord Tennyson and Wilkie Collins railed against the kakaphonia (new collective noun) of organ grinders in their neighborhood. The organ grinder and his monkey were displaced by the portable radio in the early 1950s. Too bad you can't negotiate with a boom box.

In barrel organs, pins on a rotating cylinder (the barrel) opened valves to admit air to reeds. In later versions, the crank organ was controlled by a punched paper roll similar to a piano roll. The same technology is used with the player harmonica. The manufacturer refers to this player harmonica as a "Clarola." Although shaped like a clarinet, the front bell portion of the instrument is solid wood. A prior version was shaped like a saxophone. The sound issues from the area over which the slotted paper passes. Turning the crank brings the paper slots over different harmonica reeds and rolls the paper from one spindle to another. The slots permit air from the player's breath to pass through the reed, sounding it. The melody is more sophisticated than that of a conventional harmonica because notes from any part of the 16-note range can be sounded at the same time to produce chords. The effect is close to that of an asthmatic crank organ.

A sample of the rolls: *Happy Days are Here Again, Pagan Love Song, Turkey in the Straw, Little White Lies, Silent Night.* Sorry, no Arnold Schoenberg or John Cage. The manufacturer saw nothing wrong with a tune you could whistle. These rolls sold for fifteen cents each.

The manufacturer, Q.R.S., was founded as a subsidiary of the Melville Clark Piano Company in about 1900. The company produced piano rolls. In 1918, it became independent as Q.R.S and then merged with DeVry Corporation in 1929. Q.R.S. DeVry Corporation was located in Chicago. It was there that punched roll technology was adapted for the Clarola. Q.R.S. DeVry produced cameras, projectors, radio tubes and speakers. The company survives in Buffalo, New York.

Length: 13 in.

Clarola - same type, quality and period - 2003 - $70

Pocket Watch

This is a Hampden watch. The company was founded as the Mozart Watch Co. in 1864 and renamed the Hampden Watch Company in 1877. In 1886, the Dueber Watch Case Company acquired Hampden. John C. Dueber relocated the company to Canton, Ohio in 1889. The Hampden Watch Company manufactured watches and cases until 1929 when it became so strapped for cash it paid its workers with watches who then sold them door-to-door.

In 1929, the American industrialist, Armand Hammer, purchased Hampden for $325,000. Hammer was a paradoxical character, a capitalist with a sympathy for Soviet Russia. He conducted lucrative trade with the USSR and dealt in everything from Faberge to furs to grain and liquor. He owned Occidental Petroleum Corporation. Stalin wanted his own watch factory. So, Hammer sold Hampden to the USSR and moved 28 freight cars of its watch parts, equipment and machinery to Moscow, where it was renamed the AMTORG Watch Co. Twenty one Hampden technicians moved to Moscow to set up the machinery and train Russian workers. These technicians lived in Russia for 18 months. Other watch factories were built in Russia, one of which produced this special edition timekeeper for the Red Guards, along with its technical specifications.

ТЕХНИЧЕСКИЕ ДАННЫЕ

Часы карманные механические «Молния» 3602 с боковой секундной стрелкой, 2 класса, на 18 рубиновых камнях.

Средний суточный ход часов при температуре (20±5)° С от минус 15 до плюс 40 с/сут.
Срок энергетической автономности, не менее 39 ч.
Содержание драгоценных материалов: серебра — 0,01 г.

The swirling, shimmering pattern you see on the back of the Hampden watch is called "damaskeening" by watchmakers. It is also termed "engine turning." "Damaskeening" is a corruption of "damascening," a decorative process of inlaying or welding one metal into another. Damaskeening is ornamental patterning made by moving a spinning abrasive tool across the surface and is characteristic of higher quality watches. Here, the pattern spirals out from the balance wheel.

This is a size 18 watch with 17 jewels in a nickel alloy case. The model number is 44. A distinctive feature is the rack and pinion fast/slow regulator on the bridge. Note the moon hands on the face. Based on its serial number, 2485603, this watch was manufactured in 1908.

See "Clock."

Hampden watch - same type, quality and period - 2004 - $150

Copper Tea Kettle

At the beginning of the 19th century, tea was expensive and not so pervasively popular. One opponent of the beverage states, "I view the tea drinking as a destroyer of health, an enfeebler of the frame, an engendering of effeminacy and laziness, a debaucher of youth and a maker of misery for old age." His prediction proved to be a tempest in a teapot.

By the middle of the 19th century, tea drinking was ubiquitous and the tea party had been introduced. This could be a formal social event where delicate sandwiches were served with the tea. Oliver Wendell Holmes summarized tea parties as, "Giggle, gabble, gobble, git."

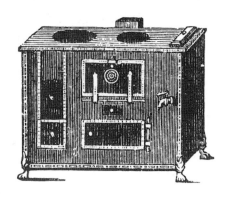

Isn't a copper tea kettle pretty prosaic technology? Yes, but it tells us a little about a 19th-century kitchen. Why does this tea kettle have an offset shoulder? The offset is a "pit bottom" or "well." When the lid of a cooking range is removed, the kettle fits into the eye or boiling hole so that the bottom is exposed directly to the flames. To the right you see a small range with the lids removed.

This tea kettle dates to the mid-19th century. The strap handle falls over and has the outline of a chef's toque. The gooseneck spout has a hinged cover and the domed lid has a scroll finial. The bottom is brazed into place with a dovetail seam. The dovetailing increases the strength of the seam, a feature common in old, heavy copper cookware. Below is a portion of such a seam.

Copper tea kettle - same type, quality and period - 2005 - $220

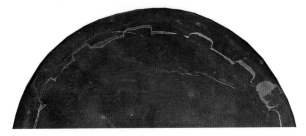

Early copper tea kettels have increased value if they carry the maker's name. Prices can be as high as $600.

Height to lid finial: 9 1/2 in.

Diameter at top: 8 in.

Diameter at bottom: 7 in.

Wallpaper Printing Cylinder

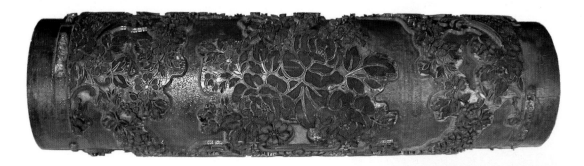

Wall decoration is a very ancient human practice. We see it in Paleolithic cave images of bison, in Egyptian temples and tombs, and in murals with more interesting subjects in the ruins of Pompeii. A contemporary wallpaper entitled "Drop cloth" consists of, you guessed it, paint spatters. Another entitled "Sharecropper" represents old newspapers and stained, cracked plaster.

The printing surface of this cylinder consists of cells outlined with brass strips similar to the cells in cloisonné enamelware. The brass strips are pounded into a wood backing and filled with felt to hold the ink or dye. Smaller printing surfaces are brass. Paper rolls over a large drum cushioned with rubber or canvas. The printing cylinder picks up ink from another roller and transfers it to the paper. This example may have been a master design cylinder including all colored areas and used as a pattern from which cylinders for each color were made. The pattern printed by this cylinder is offset columns of baskets of roses linked with wreaths of smaller flowers. A bit precious for my taste, but entirely appropriate for the period: the late 19th or early 20th century. On the right, you see a portion of the cylinder photographically unrolled. Some of these wallpaper printing cylinders have found an alternative use as lamp bases.

In the last half of the 19th century, American wallpaper designs consisted of floral motifs, geometric patterns, large wall murals and small repeated scenes. By far, most wallpaper patterns were repeated floral motifs. Colors were light and soft, similar to watercolors. The Victorians experienced an efflorescence of elaborate and garish wallpaper design. As Oscar Wilde lay dying, he said, "I am in a duel to death with this wallpaper. One of us must go."

For contemporary interior designers, the childish urge to decorate walls with grape jam has become more creative. They have used vinyl phonograph records, pie plates, playing cards, bottle caps and chicken feathers. Maybe floral wallpaper isn't so bad after all.

Length: 21 1/2 in. Diameter: 5 1/2 in.

In reverse type at end: MADE IN USA WATERFAST
UNION-MADE JOIN↑HERE

Wallpaper printing cylinder - same type, quality and period - 1999 - $70

Octagonal Barrel Rifle

Her favorite rifle was a Marlin lever-action. She was the greatest shooter that ever lived. Phoebe Moses, better known as Annie Oakley, could use a rifle or pistol with grace, artistry and consummate accuracy. Born in Darke County, Ohio, in 1860, she supported her family by her hunting skills while still in her teens. In 1885, she held star billing in Buffalo Bill Cody's Wild West show and was adopted by Sitting Bull. He named her "Little Sure Shot" and the name stuck. Annie Oakley toured Europe with the show and participated in Queen Victoria's Golden Jubilee. At Kaiser Wilhelm's invitation, she shot the ashes off his cigarette. The musical, "Annie Get Your Gun," celebrated this remarkable woman's career.

Some of the earliest rifle barrels were forged around a mandrel. Forging produced an octal barrel with flattened sides. By neatly finishing the eight flattened sides, the gun maker might save the expense of mounting the barrel on a lathe and turning it round. At some point, the octagon barrel became stylish and buyers paid a slight premium for it. B. Tyler Henry invented the lever-action rifle and first manufactured it in 1860. After working for Colt during the Civil War, John Mahlon Marlin began making firearms in New Haven, Connecticut, in 1870. His first products were revolvers and derringers. Marlin manufactured this rifle, Model 1894, from 1894 to 1905.

The rifle exemplifies the stages of industrial development. Industrial evolution begins with the craftsman who performs all steps in the production of an object from start to finish, as did the 18th-century gunsmith who made "lock, stock and barrel." In the next stage, production is segmented into specialized functions, stock carving, lock making, and barrel forging, a mode of production characteristic of most of the 19th century. Finally, industrial production involves manufacturing interchangeable parts and completing the rifle on an assembly line. Thanks to Eli Whitney, the rifle was the first such mass-produced consumer product. Production in this form dominated the 20th century.

Why include a rifle in the category of "Promoting Domestic Tranquility?" Because, in the 19th century, it was used to hunt game for food and to protect rural settlements.

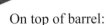

On top of barrel:

MARLIN FIRE-ARMS CO. NEW-HAVEN CT. USA
PATENTED OCT. 11 1887.
APRIL 2. 1889. AUGUST 1, 1893
32-20

The only way one could hope to match Annie Oakley's marksmanship is to shoot first and then draw the bull's-eye around the bullet hole.

See "Micrometer Calipers."

Marlin octagonal barrel rifle - same type, quality and period - 2003 - $975

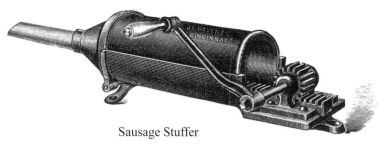

Sausage Stuffer

This model was called the "Railroad," possibly due to its rack and pinion horizontal locomotion, producing sausages like a string of freight cars.

Lemon Squeezer

More complicated than an iron maiden, this lemon squeezer (to the right) features a collapsing parallelogram.

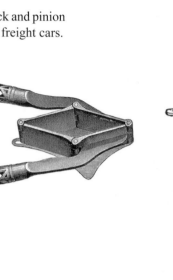

Ice Cream Freezer

In the 19th century, your banana split starts here. Ice cream was a labor-intensive product. In addition to elbow grease, essential freezing ingredients include salt and ice.

Iron Pump

This late 19th-century iron well pump is more ornate than most. It is double acting, bringing up water on both up and down strokes. Once a necessity and now almost extinct.

Roller Organ

This crank-operated organ (to the left) of 1902 has reed valves operated by a pin roller of a type familiar in music boxes. Some melodies available on rollers were *Nearer My God to Thee, Turkey in the Straw* and *Old Folks at Home.* Bach's *Toccata and Fugue* didn't make it to the roller organ hit parade.

A few more examples of domestic technology

Edison Cylinder Phonograph

This early model of Edison's "talking machine" of about 1895 may have reproduced the voice of Jenny Lind, the Swedish Nightingale. The sound would have been a mere shadow of her true voice.

Fluter

Not to be confused with a flautist, this device was a form of iron used to flute ruffles in collars and dresses, used especially when interchangeable collars were fashionable.

Tobacco Cutter

Tobacco leaves were pressed into bars or "plugs." An inch would be cut off for a customer who would break it up to smoke in a pipe or chew it. This cutter is from the late 19th Century.

Cork Puller

Corkscrews are a special category of kitchen collectibles. This model is more appropriate for a bar or restaurant with a lot of parched customers.

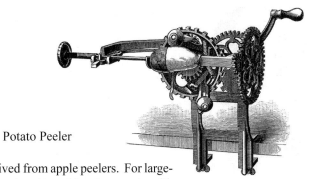

Potato Peeler

A design derived from apple peelers. For large-scale food service, it could not compete with a spud spinner, a rotating drum that tumbled potatoes and chaffed off their skins.

Weather Station

Long before the animated movement of red and blue lines across the TV weather map, this "Cottage Barometer" was used to predict local weather. The device consists of a thermometer and barometer.

Domestic technology update

The greatest transforming influence on American domestic technology was the explosive growth of household electrification. From 1930 through 1970, residential electric consumption per person increased exponentially as shown in the following graph. Domestic cooking and cleaning were revolutionized as electric appliances were acquired to help with housework. The vacuum cleaner, dishwasher and clothes washing machine were considered labor-savers, even if the electric carving knife was not.

Electric appliances relieved the American housewife of domestic drudgery and provided a huge bonus of elective time. *It ain't necessarily so.* According to sociologists Bittman, Rice and Wajcman, appliances have not reduced the hours women spend on housework.[1] They cite a 1997 Australian Time Use Survey providing detailed information on time spent on housework and the availability of household appliances. Analysis of this data showed no reduction in absolute hours of women's work in the home due to appliances. The authors theorize that any time saved by appliances was consumed by increased time spent on child care, household management and higher standards of cleanliness and comfort. A concept more familiar as: "Women's work is never done."

There is a science fiction fantasy of the completely automated household. With the combination of computer technology and electrical appliances, that fantasy draws closer to reality. You will be able to hold a conversation with your house. Voice commands will control the thermostat, television and all appliances. They, in turn, will remind you when either maintenance or payments are due.

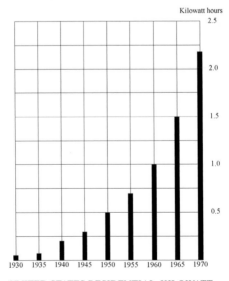

UNITED STATES RESIDENTIAL KILOWATT
HOURS CONSUMED PER PERSON

Graph based on data from the *Bicentennial Statistical Abstract of the United States*

[1] Appliances and Their Impact: The Ownership of Domestic Technology and Time Spent on Household Work, SPRC Discussion Paper No. 129, October 2003

2 AT SEA

Sextant
Octant
Box sextant
Star globe
Navigational compass
Correction dip needle
Rolling parallel rule
Taffrail log register
Angle-of-heel indicator
Telescope
Masthead light
Stadimeter
Bathythermograph
Deadeye
Ship's block
Marine propeller
Man overboard marker light
Diving hood
Fishnet floats

"At sea" refers to someone who is confused or has lost his bearings. The phrase aptly applies to the *Exxon Valdez* and the most spectacular navigational failure in recent history. The *Exxon Valdez* grounded on Bligh Reef in Prince William Sound at 12:04 a.m. on the morning of March 24, 1989, Good Friday. Eleven million gallons of oil spilled, fouling 1,300 miles of coastline. The expected economies of scale from this thousand-foot tanker became an off-the-scale environmental disaster. The *Exxon Valdez* had most of the modern navigational aids: radar, sonar, gyro compass and detailed navigational charts. It only lacked a navigator.

This section deals mainly with those instruments used to find one's way at sea. The philosophical instruments of astronomy and geography found practical use in navigation. They include the sextant and its precursors, and the compass and telescope. In the 19th century, commercial voyages could last as long as two and three years. During these voyages, the salt pork might turn rancid and weevils infest the flour, but the lives of the crew depended on navigational instruments. Since these instruments had to work, they were made of the finest materials and with great care.

Nautical Technology Time Line

Approximate Year of Manufacture of Objects in this Chapter		Year of Significant Events
	1594	Mercator publishes his atlas
	1728	Ship chronometer invented
	1734	Octant invented
	1757	Sextant invented
	1807	Fulton launches steam vessel *Clermont*
	1822	Fresnel lens invented
	1829	Diving hood invented
	1836	Screw propeller invented
	1836	Screw log invented
Ship's block	1840	
Octant	1850	
Telescope	1850	
Taffrail log register	1900	
Sextant	1910	Gyroscopic compass invented
Rolling parallel ruler	1915	Sonar invented
Box sextant	1920	
Sextant	1920	
Masthead light	1930	
Diving hood	1930	
Marine propeller	1930	
Bathythermograph	1937	
	1938	Radar invented
Stadimeter	1940	
Man overboard marker light	1942	
Dip needle	1943	SCUBA invented
	1955	First nuclear submarine launched
Star globe	1960	
Navigational compass	1960	
	1980	Global positioning system invented

Sextant

This sextant has a sectored-grid brass frame with a mahogany handle, reinforced index arm, tangent screw with spring clamp, vernier magnifier glass, silver graduated arc and vernier. The index mirror filter has four shades and the horizon glass filter has three shades. There are three scopes and two eyepieces. No original finish. The case is mahogany.

Overall length: 9 in. Chord of limb: 9 in.

Markings on arc: Y825 Heath & Co New Eltham London. S. E. 9 Made for John Lilley & Son Ltd. London & North Shields

A navigational instrument used to measure the angular altitude of a heavenly body above the horizon. The sextant has an arc of 60 degrees and can measure angles up to 120 degrees. In Latin, one sixth is "sextans."

Is a sextant worth two ears? To Captain James Cook, the great explorer, it was. In 1777, in Huahine, South Pacific, a native stole his sextant. This sextant was designed especially for Cook's expedition by Jesse Ramsden, the foremost English instrument maker. The thief was caught and the sextant returned. Cook punished the thief by having his ears cut off.

William Bligh served as Cook's sailing master on Cook's second expedition. Bligh became captain of the *Bounty* in 1787. In the South Pacific, most of his crew mutinied. He and 18 loyal crewmembers were cast adrift in an open launch. Fortunately, Bligh had a sextant and used it to navigate a voyage of 4,000 miles to Timor in the East Indies, an heroic accomplishment acknowledged by historians, but not by Hollywood.

The sextant, used by itself, can determine approximate latitude by measuring the angular altitude of the pole star. This angle subtracted from 90 degrees equals latitude. Longitude calculation requires accurate Greenwich Mean Time and information from a current nautical almanac.

Markings on plaque on index arm: "Hezzanith" Endless tangent screw   Automatic clamp Patented Semper Paratus

Heath & Co. was founded in 1845. It is listed as a nautical instrument maker in Crayford, Kent, in 1894. In the 20th century, the firm used the trademark "Hezzanith." John Lilley & Son, London, is also listed as a nautical instrument maker in 1894.

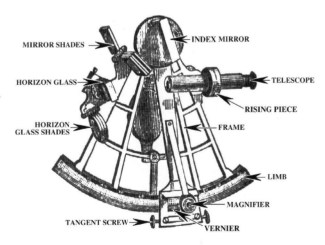

See "Octant" and "Box Sextant."

Sextants - same type, quality and period -
1977	$495
1980	$570
1997	$1,120
1999	$1,200

Octant

An octant, precursor of the sextant, is a navigational instrument used to measure the angular distance of a heavenly body above the horizon.

Here is how a secretary stalled the progress of celestial navigation for 35 years. In 1699, Sir Isaac Newton demonstrated an octant to the Royal Society. This octant had double reflecting mirrors, a key feature and Sir Isaac's unique contribution to its design. Documents describing this invention were turned over to Edmund Halley, Secretary of the Royal Society, and he misplaced them. The invention was forgotten, but the documents were discovered among Halley's papers after his death in 1742. Sorry, Edmund, no roses for you on Secretary's Day.

Meanwhile, the octant became another example of independent and concurrent invention. Timing is everything and neither John Hadley of London nor Thomas Godfrey of Philadelphia had it. Without knowledge of the other's work, each invented a version of the octant. They shared the laurels when the Royal Society awarded each a prize of £ 200 in 1734. The octant later became known as "Hadley's quadrant."

An octant has an arc or limb of 45 degrees (an eighth of a circle) calibrated to measure angles up to 90 degrees. This same instrument is sometimes called a "quadrant" because it measures a quarter of a circle, 90 degrees.

This octant has an ebony frame, ivory arc, vernier, and name plate. The vernier reads 20 to 0. The vernier is chipped. There are three mirror shades and three horizon glass shades. There is a screw adjustment for the horizon glass. The peep sight has two holes with a shield that can be moved over either hole. The brass index arm has a reinforcement strip, tangent screw and screw clamp. Mahogany keystone case. It was made in the mid-19th century.

Overall length: 13 1/2 in. Chord of limb: 11 in.

Markings on ivory name plate on crosspiece:
E & G W Blunt New York

The firm of Edmund M. and George W. Blunt (brothers) of Newburyport and New York City was established in 1824 and became Blunt and Nichols in 1866.

The dealer, Samuel Thaxter and Son, did business at 125 State St., Boston from 1825 to 1901. Dealer label inside case cover: S. Thaxter & Son. 125 State St. Boston

See "Sextant" and "Box Sextant."

Octants - same type, quality and period -
1995	$950
1997	$1,300
1999	$1,250
2003	$1,900

Box Sextant

Are we there yet? The trip seems a lot longer when you're counting white caps instead of state license plates. It's 1960 and Jean LaCombe is on his way from 50° 23' N Lat., 4° 10' W Long. to 40° 44' N Lat., 73° 59' W Long. He's competing in the first, single-handed, trans-Atlantic race. He'll spend 74 lonely days at sea in his 20-foot sailboat. There's not much room aboard. Not much room is needed for his box sextant. It's accurate, reliable and small. Jean used it to navigate the Atlantic Ocean from Plymouth, England, to New York City. He didn't win the race, but the loss was no fault of his box sextant.

Box sextants were used as lifeboat sextants and also for land surveys. Some include small telescopes, others have only a peep sight. This brass box sextant has a peep sight and two shades. A magnifier enlarges the silver graduated arc and vernier. The vernier reads 30 to 0. It was manufactured in 1918. This nifty little sextant looks like a lady's compact when closed. With so much navigational power crammed into such a little space, James Bond might have used it. William Jones of London, England, invented the box sextant in the late 18th century.

On brass lid:	Admiralty arrow (symbol)
	Stanley, London. No 3740 1918
On top of sextant:	Admiralty arrow (symbol)
	Stanley, London. No 3740 1918

Diameter: 2 5/8 in.
Height closed: 1 1/2 in.

The admiralty arrow (three wedges forming an arrow head) indicates an item was manufactured for military purposes. Stanley is a very old instrument-making firm. William Ford Stanley is listed as an instrument maker in London in 1843.

The lid, when removed, engages the bottom to serve as a handle. A paper disk inside the top of the lid lists natural tangents to a base of 100. Tangents are used in navigational computations for dead reckoning and in surveying where one's unknown position is found from three known positions.

James W. Queen & Co. Catalog 1879

Box sextants - same type, quality and period -

1977	$245
1980	$395
1991	$300
1996	$402
1999	$400

See "Sextant," "Octant" and "Dumpy Level."

Star Globe

Remember photographs of Russian civilians in 1960? Their clothing styles suggested a time warp to 1920. Soviet technology was just as anachronistic. At the same time it launched Sputnick (1957), Russia was manufacturing star globes. This star globe is interesting not because it's old (it dates to 1958), but because the Soviet Navy continued to use it long after it became as obsolete as the double-breasted suit.

Although Kurt Weil might get lost in the stars, an experienced celestial navigator could easily find his way. An inexperienced navigator, however, needed help. At most, 57 stars were used in celestial navigation. The star globe, a three-dimensional celestial sphere, provided help in finding them. In two dimensions, star charts and the Star Finder employ more contemporary methods of locating navigation stars. The Star Finder is a celestial chart on a disk over which different transparent templates are placed to locate the observer in relation to the stars, shown below. Of course, with the demise of celestial navigation, all of these methods are as dead as a Dog Star.

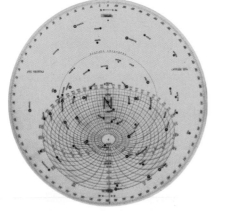

This is a Russian star globe of 1958. Constellation names are in Latin. Greek letters next to the stars indicate their relative intensity within the constellation. The outside diameter of the equatorial ring is 8 1/2 in. The metal parts are nickel-plated brass. It is in a tongue-and-groove oak case. This star globe appears to be a copy of one manufactured by Hughes & Son, London, in 1920.

Markings on a metal plate on front of case lid: 1958
No. 8333   BEC 4,4

Markings on a paper tab, probably an inspection form, on inside of lid are in Cyrillic.

The star globe is a smaller version of the celestial globe, a tool of ancient astronomy. The star globe and celestial globe are a little more difficult to interpret than star charts. With the star globe, the navigator has a divine perspective of the celestial sphere. With star charts and the Star Finder, the navigator has a human perspective, looking from the inside of the sphere upwards into the night sky. Constellations are as astrologers and the Greek Gods intended.

Star globes - same type, quality and period -
1980 $435
1999 $500

Celestial Globe

Magnetic Navigational Compass

Why is Mars lifeless? The magnetic compass points to an answer. In the earliest compasses of the Chinese, a magnetized iron needle was suspended from a thread. Arabs of the 7th century invented the compass as we know it. The study of compass error led to the discovery of magnetic declination in the 16th century. Magnetic declination is the local difference between true North and magnetic North. This difference occurs because the Earth's true poles and the magnetic poles are not the same. The study of magnetic declination and other magnetic phenomena led to the discovery of the Earth's magnetic field and the fact that the compass needle aligns itself with that field. Scientists theorize that flowing molten iron within the Earth's core produce the Earth's magnetic field.

Measurements of radiation in space show that the magnetic field shields life on Earth from lethal solar radiation. Mars has a solid iron core and has no protective magnetic field. So, that planet is lifeless because it is sterilized by lethal solar radiation. In all probability, life never existed on Mars. The Martian invasion proposed by H.G. Wells and interpreted by Orson Welles was an empty threat. Interstellar flying saucers are another matter.

This Russian ship's compass is brass and gimbaled in a tongue-and-groove pine case. The compass includes an azimuth circle with sighting vanes, filters and mirrors. This allows the navigator to sight a celestial body in the mirror and read its magnetic azimuth or bearing relative to magnetic north. The filters permit sightings of the sun.

The diameter of the compass proper is 6 3/4 in. Its height, excluding sighting vanes, filters, and mirrors, is 6 in.

The ancient wind rose on very early maps diagramed directions from which the winds blow. The points of the diagram suggested the petals of a flower or "rose." The same diagram was adopted for compass cards in the 14th century. From about 1490, the floral motif was extended by marking North with a fleur-de-lys in place of an arrow. The compass rose may be graduated in degrees, points or both. The example here is graduated in both.

See "Surveying Compass."

Compass - same type, quality and period 2003 - $500

Correction Dip Needle

A dip needle or inclination compass measures the angle between the horizontal plane and the earth's magnetic lines of force. In this diagram, you see magnetic lines of force penetrating the earth at different angles. Scientific dip needles include a magnetized needle within a vertical calibrated circle to measure these angles.

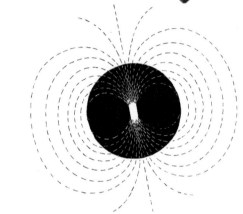

This dip needle is used in adjusting a ship's magnetic compass to correct error due to heeling (lateral roll or list) of the ship. A heeling magnet under the center of a magnetic compass is positioned according to dip needle readings.

In addition to heeling error, other sources of error include Gaussian error, residual deviation and magnetic declination. Perhaps the most egregious errors are those introduced through manufacturing. In the mid -18th century, the British Royal Navy commissioned a small squadron and equipped the ships with new compasses. The compass manufacturer's name was Tate. Tate mounted the compass cards incorrectly so that 30 degrees northeast was shown as true north. As a result, the squadron heading northward along the Atlantic coast of England, fetched up on the rocky coast of Scotland. Hence the expression, "He who has a Tate's is lost." Pardon the shaggy dog.

C.G. Conn, the manufacturer of this dip needle, is a brass musical instrument maker founded in 1879 and located in Elkhart, Indiana, and still in business. C.G. Conn temporarily converted to the manufacture of precision navigational instruments during World War II. These instruments included bombsights, altimeters, compasses and dip needles.

Length: 5 in. Width: 2 in. Height: 1 3/4 in.
Includes two bubble levels and three leveling thumbscrews.

On a brass plate on the case:

U.S. NAVY - BUREAU OF SHIPS
DIP NEEDLE
CONTRACT NO. NXS - 10424
1943
C.G. CONN LTD.
ELKHART, INDIANA

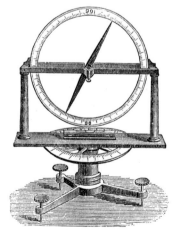

Nineteenth-century scientific dip needle

Dip needle - same type, quality and period - 2005 - $90

You have spent a week on St. Croix in the Virgin Islands where you were introduced to some avant-garde rum libations. You can no longer stand the ear-splitting roar of Bromo-Seltzer fizzing. Now, you want peace, quiet and isolation. So, you decide to sail your Bermuda-rigged ketch to Buck Island and do some scuba diving on the reef. Unrolling your navigation chart, you lay out a course line between Christiansted Harbor and Buck Island. When you set sail, what is your heading?

One or more compass roses are located on each Mercator navigational chart. They show both true north (outer circle) and magnetic north (inner circle). As navigator, you align a parallel rule with the course line. The parallel rule transfers a line parallel to itself, maintaining its initial relative position parallel to a line when moved across a chart. By moving an edge of the parallel rule across the center of the compass rose, you can read the bearing of the course line. Your heading is 72°. The parallel rule is also used with the compass rose in determining position through celestial navigation.

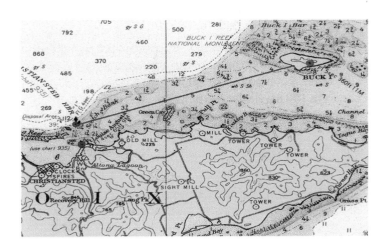

Navigational chart compass rose

This parallel ruler balances on two wheels fixed to a rotating shaft, so both wheels must roll together, thus maintaining the initial angle of the ruler. It was invented by Peter Dollond in 1770. This form of parallel ruler can roll off the chart table in heavy seas. Another and older form of parallel ruler has two separate rules linked so they can be "stepped" across the chart while maintaining the initial angle. It's more stable on the chart table. Sorry, you wont find any of Captain Morgan's treasure on the reef at Buck Island, though you might find some of his rum bottles.

Manufactured by Keuffel & Esser Co. N.Y.
No. 1758
Brass throughout.
Length: 18 in. Width: 2 3/8 in.
Early 20th century.

Rolling parallel ruler

Linked parallel ruler

Rolling parallel ruler - same type, quality and period - 2005 - $40

Encyclopedia Britannica - 10th Ed. 1903

Taffrail Log Register

"Who won?" asked Queen Victoria. "The Americans won, your Majesty." "Who was second?" "Ma'am, there is no second." In 1861, the challenger for the "One Hundred Guinea Cup" in the English regatta was *America*. It easily outdistanced a 16-boat English fleet in a stunning victory. Could this taffrail log register have been aboard America's *Reliance* when it defeated England's *Shamrock III* for the Cup in 1903?

The taffrail log measures the distance a vessel has traveled through the water. A spinner (known as a "fish") connected to the register by a cable is dragged through the water. Rotations of the spinner are recorded as distance on the register. It reads to 100 nautical miles in tenths. It is called a "taffrail" log because the register was fixed to the aft rail (taffrail) of a vessel. The ship's speed was recorded for navigational purposes in a "logbook." Later, this logbook was used to record all the events of a ship's journey, a sort of ship's diary.

Originally, a float and log line measured speed through the water (throw a log over the side and count the knots as a line pays out – the labor intensive method of measuring speed). The knots in the line became the nautical measure of speed or "knot," nautical miles per hour. Walker introduced the "patent" log in 1878. This log register has a heavy brass casing, a cast brass gimbaled mount and a white enameled face.

Overall length: 10 1/4 in.
Maximum diameter: 4 3/4 in.

On the enameled face and
top of brass casing:

Walker's patent "Cherub" (Mark II) Ship Log

A fish

This log register is a beautiful example of 19th century modern design. It is effective, functional and economical in material. There is no gratuitous ornamentation.

Angle-of-Heel Indicator

On one's "beam ends" means having hard luck and hard times. The phrase refers to the cross beams in a vessel when she is on her side. In this condition (90 degrees), the Captain doesn't need an angle-of-heel indicator to know the ship is in very serious trouble. An angle-of-heel indicator is used to measure the extent of rolling, heeling or listing. This angle-of heel indicator measures to 60 degrees port or starboard. A weighted pendulum moves the pointer.

The *Nathan F. Cobb*, a three-masted square rigged schooner was on her beam ends on December 1, 1896. She was carrying lumber off the east coast of Florida when she capsized due to gale winds and high seas. In desperation, the crew cut off the sails and masts. The water-logged vessel righted itself, but the trials of the crew had just begun. A mate and a cook were swept overboard and drowned in the storm.

The vessel grounded one thousand feet off the beach of Ormond, Florida. As the storm raged, townspeople and the U.S Lifesaving Service launched several small boats, attempting to rescue the Captain and five remaining crew. During one of the attempts, a rescuer was lost in the surge and drowned. The Captain tied himself to a life preserver with a line to the vessel and swam to a rescue boat. He finally reached shore and the remaining crew used the line, one at a time, to reach the shore.

Curiously, the *Nathan F. Cobb* was named for the owner of a salvage company who was noted for his generosity and compassion to shipwrecked sailors. It was Cobb's humanity that pioneered the way for the founding of the U.S. Lifesaving Service.

Angle-of-heel indicator:

Diameter: 7 in.
Depth: 2 3/4 in.
Brass case with white enameled dial.
Manufacturer: C. Plath, Hamburg, Germany

Carl Plath, a surveying instrument maker, purchased a navigational instrument manufacturer in 1862. With this company, he built a world-wide reputation for the quality of his instruments, especially sextants. In 1905, he adopted the Sun-Shooter logo you see on the right. It is on the dial of the indicator. His instruments were used in the navigation of the Graf Zeppelin. After World War II, C. Plath was acquired by the Sperry Marine Corporation. This example is missing maximum angle markers.

Sun-Shooter

Angle-of-heel indicator - same type, quality and period - 2009 $120

Telescope

"I call this a *device-for-making-distant-objects-appear-near*." So said Hans Lippershey of Middleburg, Holland, in 1608. He was speaking to a state commission appointed to review his patent application. They gave him 900 florins for his invention and an order for more such devices, but no patent. Their reason for this raw deal: the idea of the device pre-existed Lippershey's working example. In fact, Sir Francis Bacon had written a confused description of such a device three hundred years earlier. To add insult to financial injury, Galileo's significant improvements of Lippershey's telescope were so extensive, that Galileo was popularly accorded the laurels for its invention.

Lippershey's device was sometimes termed a *perspective* glass. Perhaps, the earliest reference to a *telescope* was in an Italian treatise on the subject of about 1655. Telescope combines two Greek roots: *tele* for "distant" and *skopos* for "one who watches."

This marine telescope or spyglass dates from the second quarter of the 19th century.

Four draw
Closed: 12 3/4 in.
Opened: 46 in.
Diameter of objective lens bezel: 2 7/8 in.
Unsigned
Mahogany barrel, objective cover, sliding eyepiece cover
Damaged soft leather case

Early lenses were sections of a sphere, introducing spherical aberration. Truly elliptical and parabolic lenses eliminated this image distortion in 1732. Since early lenses refracted (bent) light of different colors at different angles as does a prism, colored objects were not clearly defined. This problem was resolved in 1733 with the invention of the achromatic lens, lenses of different materials combined to correct color aberration. The solution of these two problems created what is, essentially, the modern telescope.

See "Spherometer" and "Binoculars."

Telescope - same type, quality and period - 1977 - $255, 1980 - $315, 2005 - $450

Masthead Light

Baruch Spinoza (1632-1677), a Portuguese lens grinder and philosopher, said we should view reality through the lens of philosophy. If we viewed reality through a Fresnel lens, we would see it in concentric rings or parallel bands.

When light radiates from a source in all directions and we need light only in a single plane, then we waste most of the light. That's the lighthouse problem, maximize light visibility to the horizon. Systems of mirrors only partially succeeded in concentrating the light. In 1822, Augustin Fresnel (pronounced "Frenell"), a brilliant French physicist and mathematician, developed his refractive lenses. His lenses concentrated light by means of circular prisms. The angles of the prisms were perfectly calculated to collimate light into a plane. Masthead lights have the same goal as the lighthouse, maximum visibility to the horizon. So, the Fresnel lens was quickly adopted for masthead lights.

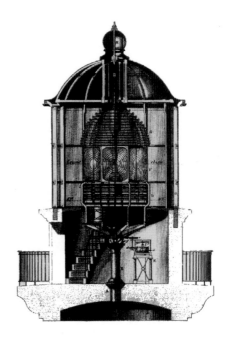

 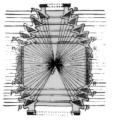

INTERNATIONAL RULES
LIGHTS AND SHAPES

Rule 2

On or in front of the foremast, or if a vessel without a foremast then in the forepart of the vessel, a bright white light so constructed as to show an unbroken light over an arc of the horizon of 20 points of the compass (225 degrees), so fixed as to show the light 10 points (112 ½ degrees) on each side of the vessel, that is, from right ahead to 2 points (22 ½ degrees) abaft the beam on either side, and of such a character as to be visible at a distance of at least 5 miles.

This light dates from the end of the nineteenth century. It's rugged and built for heavy duty. And a good thing, too. Would you want to climb to the top of the foremast to repair the light in the middle of a stormy night?

This black masthead light is sheet steel with forged handle and cast iron mounting brackets. It contains an oil lamp. The lamp is reached through a door in the back. This door has a lamp reflector attached to it. The oil lamp is gimbaled. Height: 18 1/2 in. Width: 7 in. No maker's marks.

 The Fresnel lens was also used for port and starboard lights. This mnemonic could help you remember what goes where. "There is no red port left." Clearly, green and starboard are to the right. If you're color blind, forget the mnemonic.

Stadimeter

April 26, 1952, Atlantic ocean, U.S. destroyer *Hobson* collided with the U.S. aircraft carrier *Wasp*, 176 dead.

February 10, 1964, South Pacific, Australian destroyer *Voyager* collided with Australian aircraft carrier *Melbourne*, 82 dead.

August 31, 1986, the Black Sea, the Soviet passenger ship *Admiral Nakhimov* collided with the Soviet freighter *Pytor Vasev,* 398 dead.

In fair weather, any old salt worth his salt could use a stadimeter to avoid collision. The stadimeter measures distance at sea, especially the distance between your ship and other ships. The instrument is similar to a sextant in that it has a mirror, horizon glass and telescope. To find distance, the height of the object in feet above the waterline must be known or estimated. Usually, the object is the top of the highest mast of another vessel. One enters this height on a scale by turning the end thumbwheel. Then, one sights through the telescope at the top of the object and turns the micrometer drum until the top of the object apparently moves to the waterline. Distance in yards is then read from the drum. The stadimeter was most useful in keeping proper distance during manuvers or when sailing in formation or convoy.

Modern navigational charts show the elevations above mean high water of conspicuous landmarks along the coastline. These landmarks include lighthouses, towers, smokestacks, spires, tall buildings, bluffs and mountains. With a stadimeter (or sextant), these elevations can be used to find the observer's distance from the landmark.

Radar makes the stadimeter virtually obsolete. Radar is highly accurate and there's no input other than radar reflection. Of course, someone has to be watching the radar screen.

This type of stadimeter was invented by an American naval officer, Bradley Allen Fiske (1854-1942). Since this instrument was made in 1942, it probably saw service in World War II. It is brass with a black crackle finish. It has a tongue-and-groove oak case. Length: 11 1/2 in. Width: 5 1/4 in. A brass plate on the handle reads:

STADIMETER
U.S. NAVY, BuSHIPS
N4097 1942
AJAX ENGINEERING CO.
CHICAGO, ILL

Stadimeters - same type, quality and period - 1997 - $225

Bathythermograph

Not a rocket, not a torpedo, but a device for measuring the temperature at different ocean depths. Remember the movie: *Run Silent, Run Deep*. The audience gasped when the submarine's cook drops a ladle as a Japanese destroyer listens overhead. Will it be heard? Will the depth charges strike? Clark Gable never tells you that World War II U.S. subs were equipped with bathythermographs designed to locate cold water strata (thermoclines). These strata deflect Sonar echoes and disguise the true location of submarines hiding beneath them.

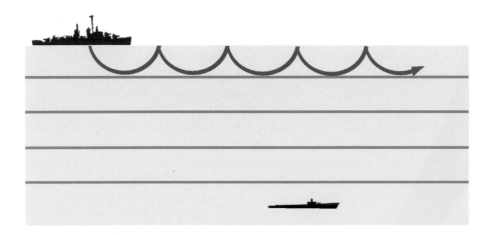

Athelstan Spilhaus invented this bathythermograph in 1936. Originally, it was towed underwater by a surface vessel for oceanographic research. It recorded sea temperature versus depth by etching a trace on a slide of smoked glass. A long, coiled Bourdon tube (see Steam Pressure Gauge) filled with a temperature-sensitive fluid reacts to changing temperature. A bellows containing a vacuum responds to changing pressure. Together, they control the stylus making the trace. This example of the Spilhaus bathythermograph or BT is an early version.

Bathythermograph: brass, height: 31 1/2 in., weight: 21 lbs., serial number 15915.

See "Self-Recording Thermometer" and "Barograph."

Bathythermograph - same type, quality and period - 2010 - $85

Deadeye

Matthew Walker holds the honor of having a knot named after him. According to a reliably apocryphal legend, Matthew Walker was a sailor awaiting sentencing for a fatal dockside brawl. The judge, a former sailor himself, had some sympathy for the defendant. He told the defendant that, if he could tie a knot the judge had never seen, he would be pardoned. Matthew Walker tied the knot shown here, and won his freedom. The Matthew Walker knot is commonly used to stop off the ends of the lanyard laced through deadeyes.

A deadeye is a disk of wood with a grooved edge, penetrated by three holes and used in pairs to tension mast shrouds or standing rigging on sailing vessels. Often, they were made of lignum vitae, an exceptionally hard and dense wood. Riggers used a lanyard laced through the deadeyes to adjust them. Turnbuckles have replaced deadeyes in modern sailing vessels. A disk, similar to a deadeye, containing a single hole, termed a "bullseye," served as a block in running rigging.

Why is this called a "deadeye?" One explanation: it reminded someone of the eye and nose sockets in the jawless face of a human skull. Another explanation: a lanyard was threaded through the holes as in the "eye" of a needle. "Dead" because it lacks the rolling sheave of a block. See "Ship's Block."

Deadeye: wood, diameter: 4 1/2 in., thickness: 3 in.

Deadeye - same type, quality and period - 2009 - $45

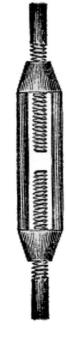

Deadeye   Turnbuckle

Ship's Block

(only a Landlubber would call it a pulley)

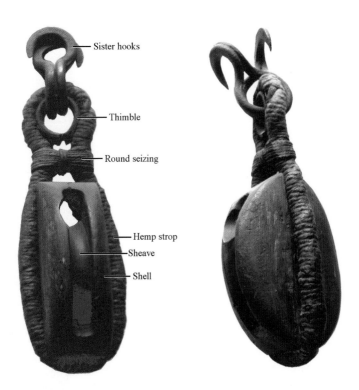

Sister hooks
Thimble
Round seizing
Hemp strop
Sheave
Shell

Who needs ship's blocks? The Royal Navy consumed 100,000 every year at the beginning of the 19th century. These blocks were handmade, expensive and in short supply. In 1807, Sir Marc Isambard Brunel designed block-making machine tools. The brilliant engineer and machinist, Henry Maudsley, built models from Brunel's designs.

Samuel Taylor, the leading supplier of blocks to the Royal Navy, haughtily declined the opportunity to build and operate machine tools based on Brunel's models, saying such tools were impractical. Samuel Bentham, Inspector-General of Naval Works, took a different view of the models and persuaded the Admiralty to build the machines. Within four years, ten Royal Dockyard workers used these machine tools to do the work formerly performed by 110 hand-skilled blockmakers. Samuel Taylor was out of business. Sir Marc's son, Isambard Kingdom Brunel, was a chip off the old block. He designed the *Great Eastern*, by far the largest steamship of its time.

This ship's block shows signs of the handwork of those technologically unemployed, but skilled blockmakers. The shell and sheave of this single block are wood. The sister hooks and thimble are hand-forged steel. Note the halyard wear at the top of the sheave. At one time, the strop was painted with pitch. The strop is hemp and has been "served," wrapped with marline.

Serving

The overall shape of the shell, a smooth ovoid ellipse, prevents the block from catching in the sheets or shrouds of the rigging. This shape is more elegantly "modern" than the shapes of contemporary ships' blocks.

Overall length: 18 in. Width: 5 1/2 in.

See "Oscillating Cylinder Steam Engine."

Ship's block - same type, quality and period - 1977 - $30

Marine Propeller

You may recall Captain Ramius aboard the submarine, *Red October*. The submarine was a terrific threat because it was engineered to eliminate cavitation and move in complete silence. Cavitation, not the type that worries your dentist, is the vacuum caused in water by the rotation of a propeller blade. It reduces propeller efficiency and creates sonic waves picked up by sonar. The shape of modern propeller blades is designed to minimize cavitation.

Of course, there are other ways of propelling a ship as shown by this engraving from *Scientific American* of 1854. "The advantages claimed by the inventor are greater speed, safety and simplicity of construction, which he is very confident will be the means of creating a complete revolution in ocean travelling." No pun intended.

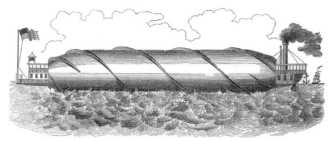

FROST'S MARINE LOCOMOTIVE

Brass three-bladed propeller, 18 in. in diameter with a pitch of 17, for a shaft size of 1 1/4 in. Older propeller blades are widest at the tip, having a roughly triangular shape. Modern, blades are widest near the center of the blade with an elliptical shape.

Markings on the boss or hub:

18X17   1 1/4   G276
FEDERAL EQIPOISE 18RH17

"Sny" is not a sly sneer. It's the upward curve of a plank at the ship's bow or the amount of twist in a marine propeller blade. For a propeller blade, sny is more precisely stated as pitch. The pitch of a blade divided by its diameter is the pitch ratio. Generally, a pitch ratio of less than one is used for high-speed propellers driven by internal combustion engines. A pitch ratio greater than one, as high as two, is used for slow-speed propellers driven by reciprocating steam engines. This propeller has a pitch ratio of 0.9, so it is appropriate for an internal combustion engine. From the direction of blade twist, we can tell that this blade rotates clockwise.

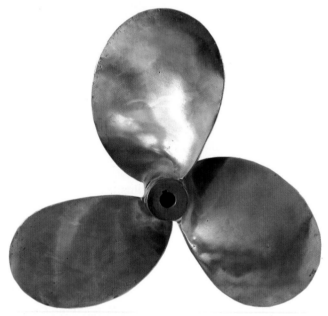

The use and shape of a propeller seems obvious to us, but this was not the case with our forebears. One of the first advocates of the screw propeller versus the paddle-wheel was John Ericsson, a Scandinavian-American naval engineer. In 1836, he took out a patent for a screw propeller and received a large payment from the British Admiralty for it. In 1839, he designed the first vessel with screw propulsion to cross the Atlantic.

Marine propeller - same type, quality and period - 1997 - $63

Man Overboard Marker Light

"He swam on mechanically in the track of the ship, sobbing quietly to himself in the misery of fear. And the stern light became a tiny speck, yellower but scarcely bigger than some of the stars, which here and there shown between the clouds.

Nearly twenty minutes passed and the man's fatigue began to change to exhaustion. The overpowering sense of the inevitable pressed upon him. With the weariness came a strange comfort – he need not swim all the long way to Suez. There was another course. He would die. He would resign his existence since he was thus abandoned. He threw up his hands impulsively and sank."

Excerpt from *Man Overboard,* a short story by Sir Winston Churchill.

Churchill describes the tragedy that the man overboard marker light is designed to prevent. This marker is also called a lifebuoy light. These lights are hung upside down on a ship's railings or attached to a life preserver. When thrown in the water, they right themselves and turn on automatically. Contemporary marker lights have plastic casings. This marker light dates to World War II.

According to Rear Admiral Austin Knight, the most immediate threat to a person falling overboard from a steamer is the danger of contact with the propellers. The individual's first instinct is to swim towards the ship, but this increases the hazard. Initially, swimming away from the ship is the safest course. A little advice in case you are in the same predicament as Churchill's character.

All brass with glass protective lens. The sheet brass casing has begun to crack, probably due to improper annealing. Bad news for the man overboard.

Nameplate missing. Uses 3.5 volt bulb.

On bottom ring ferrule: EASCO

Height: 14 in. Widest diameter: 6 1/2 in.

EASCO is a British firm that manufactured marker lights for RAF life jackets during the Second World War.

Man overboard marker light - same type, quality and period - 2006 - $40

Diving Hood

In the 19th century, the effects of pressure in underwater work (the bends) were poorly understood. The risks were staggering. Had these risks been known, many underwater projects would never have been attempted. In 1870, a bridge was built across the Mississippi River at St. Louis. Men worked in diving bells on the bridge foundations at a pressure of 50 pounds per square inch. Of 352 men working under water, 30 were seriously injured and 12 died due to pressure-related illness, almost a 10 percent casualty rate.

There is a diving suit that maintains sea-level atmospheric pressure (15 pounds per square inch) and permits the diver to descend to a depth of 2,000 feet. Joseph Peress invented it in 1935. This diving suit is made of magnesium alloy and weighs a mere 910 pounds. Its bulbous design reminds one of the Michelin Man.

Seventy percent of the Earth's surface is covered by oceans at an average depth of 2 1/2 miles and almost all of it is unexplored. Because of the problems of pressure, the conditions at great depths are just as hostile as those of outer space. Sylvia Earle said, "There are more footprints on the Moon than on the sea floor."

This diving hood differs from a diving helmet in that it is not pressurized. If the diver bends over far enough, the hood fills up with water. This is a real problem if you need to tie your shoelaces or pick up a Spanish dubloon. It is intended for shallow dives. In 1829, Augustus Siebe invented the diving hood, basically a diving bell for the head only. SCUBA has displaced this type of diving hood for shallow dives.

This diving hood is copper with brass fittings. It has grid-protected viewing ports on top, front, and both sides.

Made in 1926 - based on patent number

Height including handle: 26 in.
Width at shoulders: 12 1/2 in.
Weight: 30 lbs.

Markings on brass plate:

> DIVINHOOD Style 3
> Navy Standard
> U.S. 1195798   1595908 and Foreign Patents
> Miller - Dunn Co.
> Miami, Fla.

Diving hood - same type, quality and period -
1977 $270
2003 $700

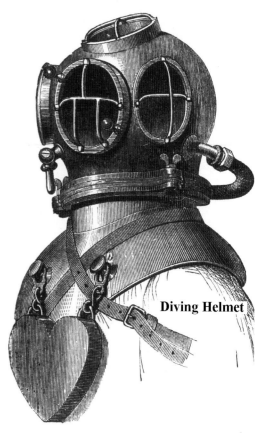

Diving Helmet

Fishnet Floats

For the edification of beachcombers and finders keepers:

Jetsam— wreckage or cargo deliberately thrown into the sea.

Flotsam— wreckage or cargo floating on the sea.

Lagan— wreckage or cargo at the bottom of the sea.

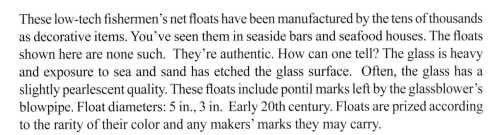

All of the above found goods were described in archaic legalese as *findals*. Now, how would you classify fishnet floats? That's right, flotsam. "Flotsam" is used metaphorically to mean useless or worthless. But, this type of flotsam, if authentic, is valued as a marine collectable.

These low-tech fishermen's net floats have been manufactured by the tens of thousands as decorative items. You've seen them in seaside bars and seafood houses. The floats shown here are none such. They're authentic. How can one tell? The glass is heavy and exposure to sea and sand has etched the glass surface. Often, the glass has a slightly pearlescent quality. These floats include pontil marks left by the glassblower's blowpipe. Float diameters: 5 in., 3 in. Early 20th century. Floats are prized according to the rarity of their color and any makers' marks they may carry.

Ancient fishermen used gourds as net floats. Today, fishermen use commercially-made cork and plastic floats. Commercial plastic floats are shaped as doughnuts, ovoids and spheres. Norwegians used large egg-shaped glass floats. Spherical glass floats were used in Canada. By far, the greatest number of glass floats originated in Japan. Many are recycled Coke bottles left by U.S. troops in occupied Japan after World War II.

These glass net floats inspired the artist in glass, Dale Chihuly. He created brilliantly colored, iridescent, large glass spheres he refers to as "Niijima Floats." Niijima is a Japanese island and the site of an international glass festival.

According to a newspaper story in *The Register-Guard* of Eugene, merchants of Florence, Oregon, have "seeded" nearby beaches with glass balls to lure beachcombing tourists. Is there no limit to human perfidy?

Marine Propellers

This is a group of 19th-century marine propellers. They are a long way from the modern variable pitch propeller that can reverse the direction of a ship without changing the rotational direction of the driving shaft.

Marline Spikes

A marline is a small line sometimes used to wrap ropes to prevent unraveling or wear (serving). Sailors and sailmakers used marline spikes in separating strands of rope for splicing.

Marine Lanterns

These 19th-century lanterns have Fresnel lenses for maximum distance visibility. The lantern on the right is a side light and would have a red or green lens.

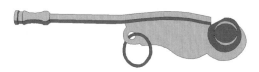

Boatswain's Pipe

A boatswain (pronounced "bosun") is in charge of deck work. He used his pipe to give orders. It's loud, shrill whistle could be heard above the sound of storm or battle. The boatswain also used it to pipe dignitaries aboard the vessel in ceremonial receptions.

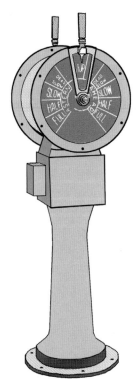

Ship's Telegraph

The captain or pilot used the ship's telegraph (to the left) to send engine commands from the bridge to the engineer in the engine room. Typically, they stood about 40 inches high. They have been supplanted by servo-mechanisms giving the pilot direct control of the engines.

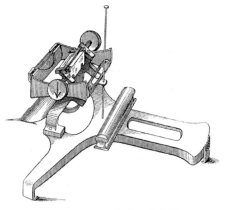

Azimuth Mirror

The azimuth mirror is placed on top of a compass to accurately determine the compass bearing of objects or landmarks. A mirror and prism reflect compass degrees on to the horizon.

A few more examples of nautical technology

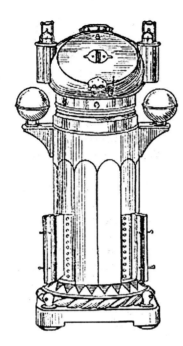

Binnacle

A binnacle is housing for the ship's compass located by the helmsman. It usually included a lamp for night light. Some binnacles had elaborate and ornate supports of mermaids or sea horses. Here, the two spheres are soft iron globes adjusted to reduce compass error. The binnacle may also include a Flinders bar of soft iron, also used to correct compass error.

Sounding Machine

Used to measure sea depths, the sounding machine (to the right) is basically a sinker on a line. The dial on top indicates the amount of line released. This hand-cranked model was displaced by electric motor driven models. Both were superseded by Sonar measurements of sea depth.

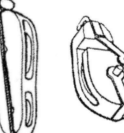

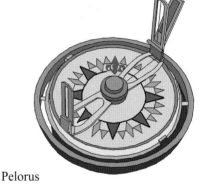

Double Sheave Block   Fiddle Block   Snatch Block

As many as 1,400 blocks could be used on a single sailing vessel. Block designs varied widely depending on their special purposes; some blocks had up to four sheaves.

Pelorus

A pelorus or dumb compass includes a compass rose, but no compass needle. By aligning North and South on the compass rose with the major axis of the vessel (the lubber line), sighting vanes are used to identify the *relative bearing* of objects or landmarks to the vessel.

Anchors

In the early 20th Century, large anchors sometimes served as lawn ornaments of New England sea-side cottages. These are 19th-century examples. The end of the anchor rope connects to a *bitt*. So, the end of an anchor rope is the "bitter end." On reaching the bitter end, you are "at the end of your rope."

Nautical technology update

In the 19th century, the reciprocating steam engine, the steam turbine and the steel hull ended the age of iron men in wooden ships. The ship's carpenter retired, sails were reefed and the Chief Engineer replaced the Sailing Master. The Navigator's complex skills remain in demand through the 20th century. In the 21st century, he retains his post and is still responsible for directing the movement of the ship, but his knowledge of stars and mathematics are superfluous.

The ancient art of celestial navigation persisted until 1993 when the global positioning system (GPS) became fully operational. This single system has rendered the sextant, the compass, the star globe, the chronometer and the nautical almanac all obsolete. Even navigation aids used for dead reckoning, such as the log, the pelorus and the stadimeter have diminished utility on a GPS-equipped vessel. Standard GPS instantly identifies the receiver's location on the surface of the Earth within a range of 33 feet. Military GPS (SPS) is even more accurate.

Here's how GPS works. Twenty four satellites with known orbits, spaced to provide worldwide coverage, transmit signals at a fixed frequency. Due to the Doppler effect, a receiver on the Earth receives signals of increasing frequency as a satellite approaches and signals of decreasing frequency as the satellite moves away. The receiver measures this shift in signal frequency from four different satellites and converts the signals into position coordinates on the Earth's surface.

Modern freighters and passenger ships navigate by means of a video display located on the bridge. A single monitor (Electronic Chart Display and Information System) with GPS and radar input shows a navigational chart and this information:

> Ship's real-time location shown on the chart
> Ship's recent track
> Planned route
> Radar overlay
> Depth sounding data
> Displays of fixed geographical electronic navigation aids
> Autopilot performance

In short, more than enough information for Christopher Columbus to tell the difference between the Bahamas and India.

3 MIGHTY IN STRENGTH AND ENDURANCE

Horizontal steam engine
Marine steam engine
Oscillating cylinder engine
Steam tractor governor
Steam engine oil injector
Steam pressure gauge
Pop safety valve
Revolution counter
Steam engine indicator
Gasket cutter
Steam whistle

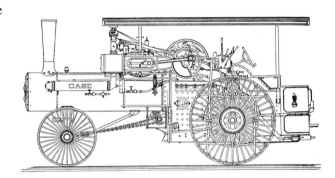

Many years ago I saw a huge steam tractor of a type used in the great plains in the 1880s and 1890s. It stood ten feet high and was almost 20 feet long, the size of a small locomotive. It was rated at 60 horsepower. Imagine the awe and pride of a 19th-century farmer in owning a traction engine with the controllable power of 60 horses *and these horses never tired.* No wonder he welcomed this great beast into his family by giving it a name. There was a sheet steel canopy over the tractor. Carefully worked into the hanging edge of the canopy with brass rivets was this legend: JOHN WILLIAMS – MIGHTY IN STRENGTH AND ENDURANCE.

Manufacturers were not awe struck by the steam engine, but they were impressed. The steam engine enabled them to locate their factories near raw materials and labor pools, a portability not afforded by waterfalls and water wheels. The result: large cost savings as steam power boomed. The objects in this section are components of steam technology. Often, they tell a fascinating story.

Steam Technology Time Line

Approximate Year of Manufacture of Objects in this Chapter		Year of Significant Events
	1781	Watt invents modern steam engine
	1784	Double-acting steam engine invented
	1785	Oscillating cylinder steam engine invented
	1788	Steam engine governor invented
	1829	Steam tractor invented
	1848	Bourdon steam pressure gauge invented
	1851	Corliss valve system invented
	1856	Sight feed lubricator invented
	1875	Pop safety valve invented
	1880	
Horizontal steam engine	1883	Steam turbine invented
	1898	Stanley Steamer invented
Oscillating cylinder steam engine	1900	
Steam engine indicator	1900	
Steam whistle	1900	
Revolution counter	1900	
Steam engine lubricator	1904	
Steam tractor governor	1907	
Steam pressure gauge	1907	
Marine steam engine	1910	
Gasket cutter	1910	
Pop safety valve	1914	

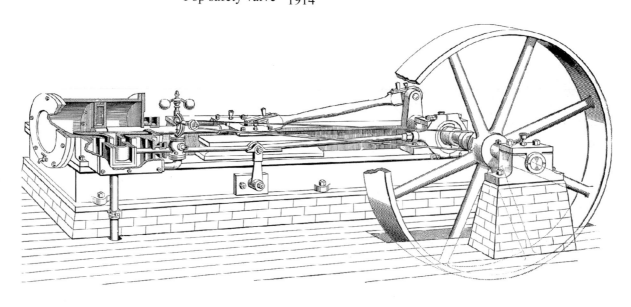

50

Horizontal Steam Engine

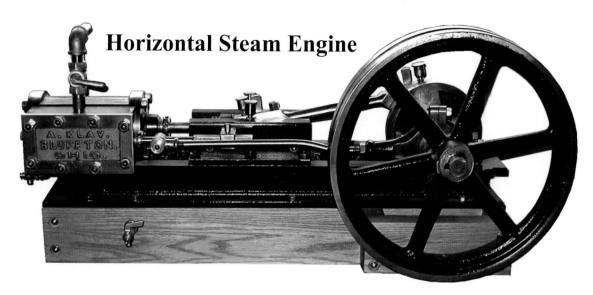

Reverand William Vere Awdrey said, "A steam engine has always got character. It's the most human of all man-made machines." This aspect of steam power makes it a metaphor for human energy, emotional or otherwise. One could get "all steamed up," go "full steam ahead," then "blow off steam," only to "run out of steam," an exhausting cycle.

This steam engine has classic design and would look great on a really large coffee table. Decorating tips aside, as a general-purpose engine, it could have been used to power a workshop or used for varied applications on a large farm. It was probably made in the last quarter of the 19th century. Below is the cover of the steam chest.

The Klay family (pronounced "Kly") from Switzerland settled in Bluffton about 1830. They were a family of mechanics and machinists. Andrew Klay, a gunsmith, operated a foundry in Bluffton before the turn of the century. In 1837, the foundry employed five workers. Many similar general purpose small horizontal or mill engines were manufactured in shops and foundries across America in the 1800's.

One indicator of age in a steam engine is the shape of the connecting rod. This one is "barrel turned," thinner at the ends with a graceful swelling at the center. Later connecting rods were straight shafts or flattened beams.

Working pressure: about 100 lbs. per sq. in.
Bore: 3 3/8 in.   Stroke: 4 1/2 in.
Flywheel diameter: 15 1/2 in.
Overall length: 36 in.

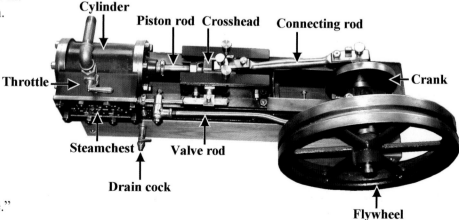

See "Marine Steam Engine."

Horizontal steam engine - same type, quality and period - 1999 $1,500

Marine Steam Engine

Remember the *African Queen?* It was powered by an engine not too different from this one. Charlie Allnut kicks the boiler and explains that if he doesn't, it will blow up. The safety valve is accidentally jammed with a screw driver.

Miss: "Mr. Allnut, why don't you dismantle the safety valve and remove the screwdriver?"

Allnut: "Well, Miss, I kinda like kickin' it. It's all I've got."

A brief insight into the loneliness of our scruffy hero.

Steam engine boilers had at least one safety valve and, often, had two. Unless properly maintained and operated, boilers were extremely dangerous. Boiler explosions in the age of steam were common and frequently fatal. Charlie Allnut's bravado on the silver screen would be flirting with death in reality.

This engine powered a launch of about 25 feet in length.

Overall height: 30 in.
Bore: 3 in. Stroke: 4 in.
Approximate working pressure: 100 psi
Approximate speed: 300 rpm
Stephenson-type reversing gear
Double acting

Steam engines of this size and type powered small launches in lakes, rivers and coastal waters up to the end of the 19th century. This steam engine is known as an OCLE (Open Column Launch Engine). It turned a propeller (relatively slowly) of about 18 to 24 inches in diameter. One had a choice of fuel for the boiler. Firewood was cheap and quiet, but if you had to carry it, the bulk severely limited one's cruising range. Coal was more efficient, but was dirty, producing soot and heavy black smoke. Oil was most efficient, but because of burner nozzle design, it made a very loud and unpleasant roar. Take your pick.

We can find the indicated horsepower for this engine using the preceding data and a simple formula. **P** is pressure in pounds per square inch (100). **L** is length of stroke in feet times two (.66). **A** is the area of the piston in square inches (7). **N** is number of revolutions per minute (300).

I.H.P = PLAN/ 33,000
I.H.P = (100 x .66 x 7 x 300)/33,000 = 4.2 horsepower

A gasoline engine of the same size and weight would produce about 150 horsepower. *Sic transit* steam engine.

We still depend on steam. Nuclear reactors heat water, converting it to steam. The steam drives turbines connected to generators, producing electricity so we can watch television re-runs of the *African Queen.*

See "Horizontal Steam Engine" and "Pop Safety Valve."   Steam engine - same type, quality and period - 1997 - $850

Oscillating Cylinder Steam Engine

The largest oscillating cylinder steam engine ever built powered the paddlewheels of the *Great Eastern*. The *Great Eastern* was no misnomer. It was a stunning engineering achievement and a magnificent vessel. It was the greatest steamship of the 19th century. Launched in 1860, its gross tonnage went unchallenged until 1903. It had a length of 692 feet. Its side paddlewheels were 56 feet in diameter. These were driven by four oscillating cylinder steam engines. Each cylinder with piston and piston rod weighed 38 tons. The *Great Eastern* had a short, unprofitable career as a passenger steamer and then, because of its huge capacity, the ship was used to lay telegraph cable. With a crew of 500, it laid a total of five trans-Atlantic cables.

Great Eastern

William Murdoch, an associate of James Watt, invented the oscillating cylinder steam engine in 1785. This is an oscillating cylinder steam engine, a working model complete with boiler. It dates from the late 19th or early 20th century.

This model is all brass, excepting the copper tubing. Height: 16 in. No maker's marks.

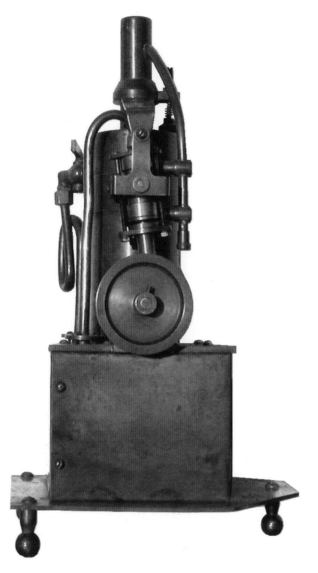

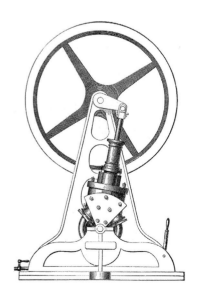

Take a close look at the cylinder above the flywheel. In this design, the cylinder rocks back and forth on trunnions. There is no connecting rod and crosshead. The piston rod connects directly to the crank behind the flywheel. Why use this configuration? Engineers supposed that eliminating the connecting rod and crosshead and their friction would greatly increase efficiency. However, the energy lost in rocking the heavy cylinder back and forth more than offset energy savings from reduced friction. Another problem with this design was preventing steam leakage at the trunnions and valve.

See "Ship's Block" and "Testing Set."

Oscillating cylinder steam engine - same type, quality and period - 2001 - $650

Steam Tractor Governor

This is a Pickering steam tractor governor. It controls the steam to assure a pre-set and constant speed when the load on the steam engine can vary from no load to full load. Why would you want this control?

It's 1895 and you've spent an exhausting week in the hot sun on the midwest plains harvesting your wheat. Now, you're using your steam tractor to power a threshing machine. Farm hands pitch-fork the crop into the threshing machine as you throttle the engine, but you're distracted when a bull escapes from a nearby pasture. You take your hand from the throttle and climb down from the tractor as the thresher finishes the last load. With no load, the steam engine speeds up. It races faster and faster. You're too far away to stop it. Parts fly from the thresher. Before you can throttle down, it's shaken into a pile of junk. A governor would have saved your thresher. No bull.

A governor controls the speed of the steam-engine threshing by throttling or limiting the amount of steam admitted to the cylinder. The essential parts of a throttling governor consist of balls which tend to fly apart by centrifugal action. Through linkage, this movement partly closes the valve.

This governor is of cast iron and steel. It has three balls controlled by an adjustable spring. Spring steel bands support the balls. The Pickering Governor Company of Portland, Connecticut, manufactured this governor, marked with a patent date of 1907.

Overall height: 20 in.
Maximum width including drive shaft: 14 in.

A cut away view of the governor is shown here.

The governor was the first automatic feedback device of the industrial revolution, controlling speed by using variable centrifugal force and the constant force of gravity. By assuring work at a constant speed despite changing load, this governor outperforms anyone elected to the office.

Governor - same type, quality and period - 1999 - $150

54

Sight Feed Lubricator

No, this is not an industrial espresso coffee maker. It really is a steam engine oil injector or sight-feed lubricator. As the age of steam reached its climax at the end of the 19th century, steam engines were oiled with these lubricators. Grease makes things go faster with less effort. Greased lightening is presumably speedier than the more pedestrian form. Similarly, the hand whose palm has been greased acts more quickly. The first squeaky wheel to get the grease was on an Egyptian chariot. The ancient Egyptians used beef and mutton tallow to lubricate axles. In 500 B.C., the Greeks used petroleum for the same purpose. Until the last quarter of the nineteenth century, animal fats and vegetable oils were the most common lubricants. With these lubricants, a heated steam engine probably had the savory bouquet of a greasy spoon.

What could force oil into a steam line against a pressure of 300 pounds per square inch? Condensed water. Steam was admitted to the bottom of the injector chamber where it condensed. This forced oil floating above the condensate into the steam line where it mixed with steam to lubricate valve and piston. Lubricators of this size were used only on very large steam engines.

Made of heavy cast and machined brass, this lubricator has six valves to control the flow of steam, oil and water. Four of these valves have wood handwheels (the injector was hot). There are two glass sight gages to check oil and water levels.

Overall height: 17 in.

This lubricator is both an artifact of the industrial revolution and a gleaming structure of glass, brass and wood.

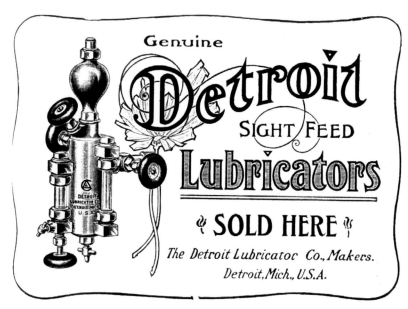

The Engineer December 1904

Steam Pressure Gauge

This gauge employs the Bourdon tube principle. The gauge contains a flattened tube bent into a semicircle. When the tube is pressurized, the tube tends to straighten. A lever and rack and pinion linked to the tube moves the pointer around the dial. The principle of the Bourdon tube is familiar in the unrolling paper party whistle, possibly used in the revelries of Diamond Jim Brady.

Here is a short tale of gauges and gluttony. Eugene Bourdon (1808-1884) received a French patent for his pressure gauge in 1849. Edward Ashcroft purchased the American patent rights to the Bourdon gauge in 1852. Pressure gauges are still manufactured under the Ashcroft name. A railroad supply company, Manning, Maxwell and Moore, purchased Ashcroft's interests in 1880. The gauge was a leading product of Manning, Maxwell and Moore.

A top salesman of the company was James Buchanan Brady. In 1912, he became vice president of the company. His earnings as a salesman enabled him to purchase manufacturing firms supplying the fast-growing railroad industry and Jim Brady became a multi-millionaire. He collected diamonds, hence his nickname, Diamond Jim. Diamond Jim Brady was a Broadway *bon vivant*, throwing lavish parties and dating showgirls. He was a gourmand with a gargantuan appetite. His gastronomic gauge was a four-inch gap between his belly and the table. He would eat until his girth filled the gap. His huge appetite brought him fame, obesity and an early death in 1917.

Steam gauges should read up to 1 1/2 to 2 times the working pressure of the engine. Since this gauge reads to 1,000 pounds per square inch, it was intended for a steam engine with a working pressure of about 500 pounds per square inch. This gauge has a bronze case and bezel. The face is nickel plated with a satin finish.

On the face: The Ashton Valve Co. Boston. Mass.

Based on the serial number, 118 673, this gauge was made in 1907. The Ashton Valve Co. had been making steam and air gauges, whistles and valves since 1875.

Diameter: 3 3/4 in.
Thickness: 1 1/2 in.

The gauge shown above includes two C-shaped Bourdon tubes. See "Barograph" to learn about the Vidie vs. Bourdon patent flap.

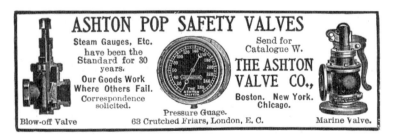

Engineer and Steam Engineering 1905

Pop Safety Valve

The *Sultana* was a large Mississippi side-wheeler headed north. She left Vicksburg overloaded with 1,866 Union soldiers, 70 cabin passengers, and a crew of 85. The Union soldiers, enfeebled and undernourished, had just been released from the horrors of Confederate prison camps. Near Memphis, Tennessee, on April 27, 1865 at about 3 a.m., a boiler exploded. The terrific blast broke the vessel in half and took the lives of 1,238 victims. This was the most catastrophic boiler explosion in history.

A number of factors contributed to this disaster, but an official inquiry concluded that one of the most important was excessive boiler pressure. Even after this event, the carnage of boiler explosions continued. From 1886 to 1892, boiler explosions killed 1,500 in the United States. In one instance, reliable measurements showed that the force of a boiler explosion hurled the boiler 1,600 feet vertically into the air. When water converts to steam, its volume expands 1,700 times. Without provision for excess pressure, a short count down to boiler lift-off is almost certain. Eventually, safer boiler engineering and safety regulation enforcement reduced the death toll. But this was due to economic, rather than humanitarian motivation. Boiler insurance companies were the prime instigators of safer boiler design and practices. The features of safe boiler design included the pop safety valve.

This type of spring-loaded safety valve replaced weighted-lever safety valves, a mechanism prohibited as unreliable. The valve automatically opens and relieves boiler pressure when steam in the boiler reaches a pre-set level. The lever releases steam pressure in a daily test to assure the valve is clear and operating correctly.

All brass. Height: 9 1/4 in. Widest diameter: 2 7/8 in.

Stamped on body: AMERICAN STEAM GAUGE & V. MFG. CO. BOSTON.

The American Steam Gauge & Valve Mfg. Company held gauge patents as early as 1903. It exhibited its products at the Universal Exposition in St. Louis in 1904. The company manufactured gauges and valves in Boston Massachusetts from 1914 to 1936.

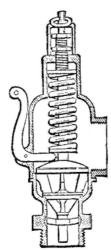

Pop safety valve - same type, quality and period - 2004 - $40

Pop safety valve mechanism

Revolution Counter

"Good God, Scotty, I'm paying three dollars a ton for coal. That steam engine goes through dollars like crap through a goose. I'm damned if I can stay in business at this rate. For Chrissake, can't you make it more efficient?" Scotty's problem: maximize horsepower and minimize cost. To adjust the steam engine, he needs to calculate efficiency. To calculate efficiency, he needs to know engine speed. To find engine speed, he needs a revolution counter. Then, he can adjust the engine. Or, as a devout Presbyterian, he could complain to the shop steward about the boss's violations of the Third Commandment.

Before the invention of the tachometer, the Engineer used this revolution counter and a watch; a stop watch if he had one, to calculate speed. The lever on the counter was temporarily linked to some reciprocating part of the steam engine.

This revolution counter is cast iron, nickel-plated, and reads to five digits in oval glass windows. The counter is reset by turning the square shafts under each digit window. Markings cast into the face read: G.P.P.Co. It was manufactured in about the last quarter of the 19th century.

The counter is mounted on an oak base. These are the dimensions of the counter proper:

Length: 8 1/4 in. Height: 2 1/4 in.
Overall thickness: 2 in.

In this counter, the Victorian *horror vacuui* asserts itself by cluttering the face of the counter with curlycues. A feature absent in a later counter shown at right.

See "Speed Indicator."

From

HAWKINS'

INDICATOR CATECHISM.
A PRACTICAL TREATISE

FOR THE USE OF ERECTING AND OPERATING ENGINEERS
SUPERINTENDENTS, STUDENTS OF
STEAM ENGINEERING, ETC.
BY
N. HAWKINS, M. E.
1903

REVOLUTION COUNTERS.

In high-speed engines it is difficult to count the number of revolutions; hence a revolution counter, as in Fig. 54 is employed.

These possess the advantage of recording the revolutions made for any length of time, and during indicator tests of importance and of long duration, they are almost indispensable.

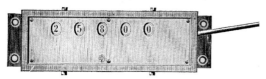

Fig. 54. REVOLUTION COUNTER.

Steam Engine Indicator

With its gleaming, nickel-plated surface, this indicator looks more like a surgical instrument than an engine room tool. It does serve a diagnostic purpose in examining steam engine performance. You may very well wish that your doctor's diagnosis from an EKG was as unambiguous as this analysis of an indicator card from a sick steam engine. The prognosis: replacement by a diesel.

"The admission is late, the steam line wire drawn and the cut-off slow at about 1/3 stroke. The piston is leaking very badly as indicated by the sudden dropping of the expansion line. The release is late, beyond the center, causing a loop which is due to the compression of the steam in the cylinder until the exhaust valve opens. There is some back pressure."

Hawkin's Indicator Catechism, 1903

Steam engine indicator card
showing very poor performance

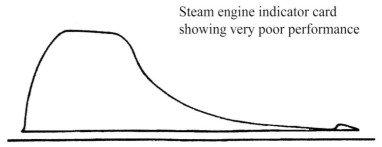

Pity the steam engineer obsessed with fuel efficiency and frustrated by so few variables under his control. Engine seals and packing had to be tight and appropriate, but adjustments were basically limited to valve cut-off, lap, and lead. To guide these adjustments, he used the steam engine indicator.

The indicator is used to measure and analyze steam engine efficiency. When attached to the engine, the indicator charts the change in pressure within a cylinder over one cycle. The figure charted is closed and the larger the area, the greater the engine efficiency. The area of the closed irregular figure is measured with a planimeter.

This indicator is made of nickel-plated brass.

Maximum height: 8 1/4 in. Maximum width: 4 1/2 in.

Markings on indicator frame:

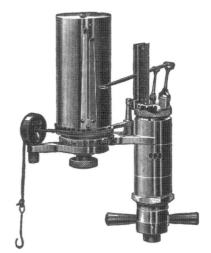

> (patents for Great Britain and U.S.A. from Dec. 10, 1878 No 7168 through April 3, 1900)
> THE "TABOR"
> The Ashcroft Mfg. Co. Bridgeport Ct. U.S.A.

See "Steam Pressure Gauge" for information about Ashcroft. Also, see "Planimeter."

The walnut case has a compartment in the lid containing three walnut pulleys. The lower compartment contains springs, valves, oil bottle, screw driver, wrench and other parts.

Steam Engine Indicators - same type, quality and period - 1977 - $77, 1999 - $200

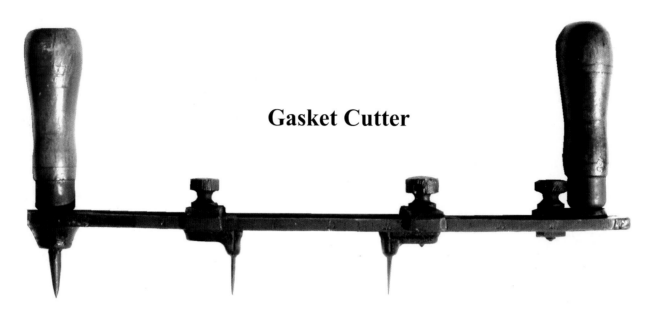

Gasket Cutter

Remember the classic Hollywood "slow burn." It was comedy in black and white. Oliver Hardy, Billy Gilbert and Leon Errol were masters of the art. Mild irritation turns to annoyance which escalates to anger, then impotent rage, all without a sound. Then, the comedian would "blow a gasket."

Gaskets contain the pressure. They seal joints at cylinder heads and at pipe and valve flanges. If part of the gasket blows or fails, the steam leaks, the pressure falls and the engine stops. Early gaskets were made of greased leather or tallowed hemp. Later gaskets were composed of felt, rubber, or a rubber-asbestos compound. High-temperature gaskets were made of a soft metal such as copper.

This gasket cutter cuts circular gaskets up to 20 in. in diameter. The two sliding cutter knives were adjusted for the external and internal gasket diameters using a scale on the edge of the bar and then the knives were locked in place. The point on the left was inserted into the sheet gasket material and the knives were rotated around the point by moving the grip on the right. After the gasket was cut, one used a punch to make bolt holes.

From 1869 forward, you could find gaskets in the kitchen. Rubber gaskets were part of the Mason jar canning process. A screw lid compressed the gasket over the mouth of the jar. This was a big improvement over a wax seal and wax paper or a wire clamp over a glass lid.

"Gasket" derives from the French, *garcette,* for ropes end. Old ropes were used as gasket material. The term has a more abstruse use.

A fractal is a mathematically generated image such that the unit parts are replicas of the whole. Waclaw Sierpinski, a Polish mathematician, invented a triangular fractal with smaller triangles punched out of it. This is one of the simplest fractals and is known as "Sierpinski's gasket." Here is the gasket. Note that the *pattern* of triangles is repeated to build up the fractal. The fractal maintains its shape from an infinitesimal to an infinite number of units. That is, unless, Sierpinski blows his gasket.

Gasket cutter of the early 20th century. No maker's mark.

Length: 11 in. Width: 1 1/4 in.

Gasket cutter - same type, quality and period - 2005 - $40

He was goin' round the bend doin' ninety miles an hour
When his whistle, it began to scream
He was found in the wreck with his hand on the throttle
He was scalded to death by the steam

From the folk song, *Wreck of the Old 97*

Locomotive Steam Whistle

Steve, the Engineer in the song, was preoccupied. He was probably unaware that the pitch of the whistle was determined by the length of the air column (or steam column) and its sound quality determined by the shape of that column. The shape determines the particular harmonics (frequencies that are multiples of the pitch) emphasized by the whistle.

Steam whistles are of two types: bell and organ. This is a bell whistle. The valve releases steam all around the bottom of the bell or tube. The organ whistle has a diagonal segment cut from the bottom of the tube, like organ pipes or the pipes of a calliope. An organ whistle may sound different notes at the same time if it has two or more cut outs (termed a "chime" whistle). Many locomotive whistles are bell whistles. Steamship whistles are usually organ whistles.

Organ whistle

This whistle bell is brass and the valve and valve lever are cast bronze. Its height is 12 inches. The valve diameter is 3 inches. The valve body is numbered 5552-1 and the valve lever is numbered 5552-4.

Why does the valve lever have such a graceful curve? Castings have low strength compared to forgings. Castings fracture rather than flex. Based on product recalls (just kidding), manufacturers added length to narrow castings, especially spokes, cranks and levers, to help them absorb shock and prevent breakage. By using curves, you could increase shock absorption without extending functional length. Hence, the elegant curves in these valve levers.

Steam Pressure Gauges

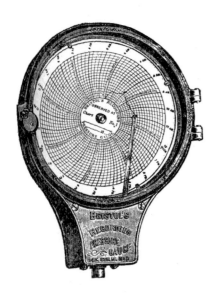

Where highly reliable steam pressure was needed, that pressure might be monitored by the gauge on the left. This late 19th-century clock-driven gauge includes paper charts and a recording stylus. A Bourdon tube moves the stylus. The chart rotates once in 24 hours.

On the right is a florid and patriotic pressure gauge of 1854 ("E Pluribus Unum" cast on the base). Not an example of strict functionality. The steam engine had been in use long enough to bear up under ornamentation. See "Steam Pressure Gauge."

Steam-Driven Crosscut Saw

A steam-powered crosscut saw of the late 19th century. Here, the reciprocating action of the steam piston applies directly to the motion of the saw. You have heard of the steam drill that John Henry beat. Could this be the steam saw that Paul Bunyan beat?

Boiler Water Injector

Also termed an inspirator, this device uses steam to inject feed water into the boiler, overcoming the steam pressure within the boiler.

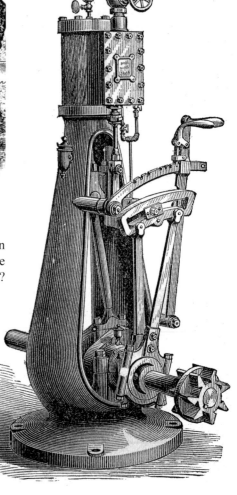

Bottle Frame Engine

This vertical bottle steam engine was so-called because its frame resembles the shape of a bottle. In this engine, the cross-head guides are not adjustable but are milled into the frame. It has a Stephenson-type reversing gear and probably drove a launch.

A few more examples of steam technology

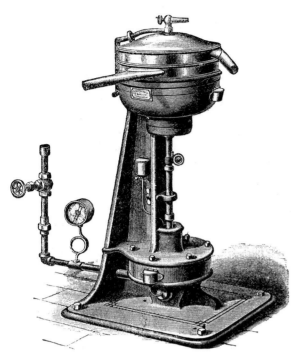

Cream Separator

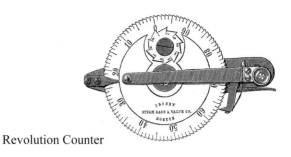

Revolution Counter

The revolution counter (above) was attached to some reciprocating part of the steam engine. It was used to find revolutions per minute in determining engine efficiency.

This is a De Laval creamer of about 1895. It separates cream from milk through centrifugal force, spinning the heavier milk into a perimeter chamber and leaving the cream in a central chamber. It is driven by a steam turbine in the base. Carl Gustaf De Laval (1848-1928) pioneered steam turbine technology and scaled up from creamer to steamer, manufacturing steam turbines for ship propulsion. Some of these obsolete creamers have found alternate use as rural flower planters. See "Milk Testing Centrifuge."

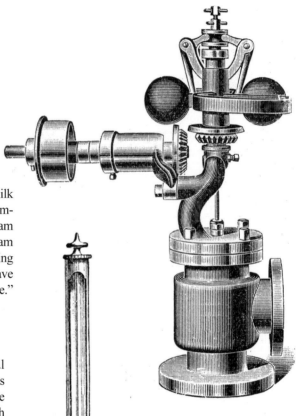

Boiler Water Gauge

Boiler water gauges (to the left) are critical safety devices. Without water, boiler plate heats up, weakens and boiler explosions ensue. These gauges must be strong enough to contain high boiler pressures. This gauge dates from about 1904. See "Pop Safety Valve."

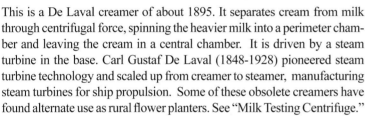

Steam Engine Governor

Another form of steam engine governor (above) of about 1904. Because the centrifugal force of the flying balls is controlled by heavy springs rather than by gravity in this governor, it can be used in any position.

Manometer Steam Pressure Gauge

In this gauge (to the right), the pressure of steam on a mercury reservoir compresses an air column and raises mercury in the gauge. This form of gauge was used in the late 19th century.

Steam technology update

The age of the reciprocating steam engine ran out of steam in three stages. First, the electric motor replaced the steam engine in manufacturing, then the steam turbine replaced the reciprocating steam engine in steamships and finally, diesel-electric locomotives replaced steam locomotives.

The conflux of three developments, all occurring within the last ten years of the 19th century, doomed the factory reciprocating steam engine. These were the electric motor, turbine electricity generation and alternating current distribution. Improvements made the electric motor practical as power for individual factory tools. It replaced the centralized mechanical power of steam engines, along with the line shafting and belt pulleys used to distribute mechanical power within the factory. The electric motor was feasible only because of cheap electric power generation and distribution. Steam turbines cost less to operate than reciprocating steam engines for power generation and so displaced those engines in electrical power plants. Alternating current permitted efficient centralized power generation with power distribution over large areas. As a result, large, turbine-driven, high-voltage, alternating current power plants replaced the many smaller electrical plants required for low-voltage direct current distribution. These developments eliminated the factory steam engine and virtually put the stationary steam engineer out of business.

At the beginning of the 20th century, the steam turbine was developed to the point where it was much more efficient than the reciprocating steam engine and, when used to power vessels, enabled much higher speeds. In addition, it was smaller and lighter than the reciprocating steam engine. Accordingly, the steam turbine was quickly adopted by most navies. The passenger ships *Mauretania* and *Lusitania* were built in 1907 with steam turbine power. The *Mauretania* held the trans-Atlantic speed record for the next 20 years. In the following decades, steam turbines gradually replaced the reciprocating steam engine in merchant and passenger shipping.

The steam locomotive evokes more nostalgia than any other steam technology. Many of us can remember the sound of the steam whistle and the sight of a series of steam puffs rising above a line of trees as a steam engine passed in the distance. In 1925, the American Locomotive Company sold its first diesel-electric locomotive to the Central Railroad of New Jersey. The diesel-electric locomotive was improved in efficiency and made lighter in weight in the 1930s. It saved labor cost in that no fireman was required to move coal; only an engineer was needed. A number of diesel-electric locomotives could be coupled and all operated by a single engineer in the first locomotive. Although the steam locomotive was the prime mover during the Second World War, streamliners and freight trains were increasingly drawn by diesel-electrics. The last American steam locomotives were built in 1949 and so the fire-breathing iron horse lost the race.

4 FRANKLIN'S FOLLY

Direct current ammeter - Thompson
Direct current ammeter - Whitney
Alternating current ammeter
Voltmeter
Testing set
Telegraph key
Electric motor
Electric drill
Slide projector
Magneto
Marine searchlight
Temperature potentiometer
Radio navigation indicator
Electric razor
Blasting machine

It was Hollywood and not Mary Shelley that infused life into the Frankenstein monster through lightning. Benjamin Franklin had a much better understanding of lightning than either. Some described Franklin's electrical experiments as folly when, in June of 1752, he flew a kite with a grounded key attached to the kite string in a thunderstorm. He proved that lightning was nothing more than an electrical discharge. He was smart enough to control the wet kite string with a strip of non-conducting silk. This and other experiments led him to invent the lightning rod, thus enriching insurance companies for centuries to come.

Franklin conducted his experiments in the middle of the 18th century, but electricity was not scientifically understood until the first part of the 20th century. We are still confused by electrical phenomena. Keith Waterhouse speaks for many of us in saying, "...what with having perforce to change a light bulb here and tune in a transistor radio there, I have picked up a pretty sound working knowledge of electrical matters. It is not comprehensive, God knows - I still can't fully understand why you can't boil an egg on an electric guitar..."

In the 19th century, managing electricity was so arcane that electrical devices were left well enough alone by Victorian decorators. As you will see in this section, these devices have functional and simple designs.

Electrical Technology Time Line

Approximate Year of Manufacture of Objects in this Chapter	Year of Significant Events
	1752 Franklin invents lightening rod
	1800 Volta invents battery
	1827 Electric motor invented
	1832 Dynamo invented
	1834 Electric motor invented
	1837 Telegraph invented
	1878 Incandescent electric light invented
	1884 Transformer invented
Direct current ammeter	1886 Portable DC ammeter invented
	1888 AC motor invented
	1893 Photoelectric cell invented
Voltmeter	1898 Loudspeaker invented
Alternating current ammeter	1903
	1904 Diode vacuum tube invented
Electric motor	1905
Magneto	1905
	1906 AM radio invented
	1907 Electric amplifier invented
Marine searchlight	1910 Neon lighting invented
Testing set	1915
Blasting machine	1915
Electric drill	1917
Slide projector	1920
Telegraph key	1920
Temperature potentiometer	1920
Electric razor	1932
Radio navigation indicator	1943
	1948 Transistor invented
	1958 Integrated circuit invented

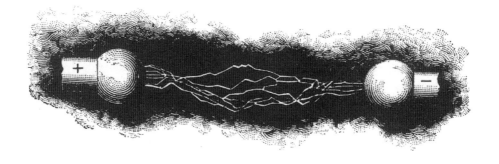

Direct Current Ammeter - Thompson

"Igor, quickly, we need more power."

"How much power, Master?"

"One thousand ..uh..uh..oh.. what d'ya call 'em?"

The first step in controlling anything is to name it. The next step is to measure it. The names of electrical units of measure memorialize the scientists who sought to control electricity: Georg Simon Ohm, Alessandro Volta, Charles Coulomb and André-Marie Ampère.

Am'me-ter (-me-ter), n. (Physics) A contraction of amperometer or ampèremeter.

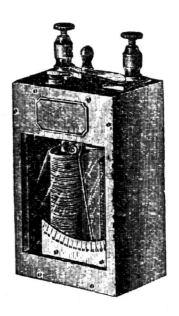

Height: 6 1/2 in.
Width: 4 1/4 in.
Thickness: 3 in.

An ammeter measures the strength of current in amperes. In this ammeter, the current in a coil moves a steel disk by induced magnetism, the disk being connected to the indicator needle.

Ampère's Rule states: "If a man is imagined to be swimming in the direction of the current flow and facing the magnetic needle; then the north pole will be deflected toward his left hand, the south pole being deflected in the opposite direction." We're not kidding.

This direct current ammeter has three green silk-covered coils and a graduated brass scale of 0 to 80. There are two brass thumb-screw terminals and a three-pole switch. The case is walnut with a calibrating screw in the back. It dates from about the fourth quarter of the 19th century. The meter has a nickel-plated brass cast plaque on the front.

Beginning in 1880, Elihu Thompson and Edwin W. Rice worked together inventing and manufacturing electrical regulators, meters and other electrical equipment. Eventually, both men joined the General Electric Corporation.

This ammeter is made of the best materials. It is solid and heavy as befits the rough usage it could encounter in Doctor Frankenstein's laboratory.

See "Alternating Current Ammeter" and "Voltmeter."

Ammeter - same type, quality and period - 1999 - $100

Could DNA, or even a soul, be trapped in amber? As we learned in the movie *Jurassic Park*, amber could contain the DNA of Tyrannosaurus Rex. Thales (624-546 BC), a Greek philosopher, studied the attractive properties of amber or *elektron* in Greek. He attributed these properties of amber to a soul within the amber. In 1600, William Gilbert, an English scientist, conducted similar studies of amber and coined the word "electric" to describe its attractive properties.

So, *elektron* lent its name to the electron flow studied by André-Marie Ampère (1775-1836). The ampere, from his name, is the unit of measure for electrical current as indicated by an ammeter.

This ammeter is the exception that proves the rule of austere functional design for electrical equipment. It sports surface ornamentation of Victorian filigree, filigree suitable as a setting for amber.

Direct Current Ammeter - Whitney

The manufacturer of this ammeter, Whitney Electrical Instrument Company, was incorporated in 1891 and located in Penacook, New Hampshire. The Company exhibited its meters at the St. Louis Exposition of 1904.

Compare the scale of this DC ammeter with that of the AC ammeter on the next page. The DC ammeter has constant calibration intervals while the AC ammeter has a diminishing geometrical scale. These scales distinguish early AC and DC ammeters.

Markings on dial: Ammeter For Direct Current No. 15687

Cast into aluminum case: Whitney Electrical Instrument Co.

Dimensions of mahogany base. Height: 6 1/8 in. Width: 6 1/4 in.

Overall depth: 3 1/4 in.

The Whitney Electrical Instrument Company, located in New Hampshire, held ammeter patents as early as 1893.

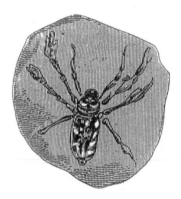

Arachnid in *elektron*

Ammeter - same type, quality and period - 2007 - $30

For Edison and Tesla, AC/DC had a completely different meaning than it does in current parlance. AC versus DC was the crux of a bitter feud. Thomas Edison supported and designed for the status quo: DC power distribution. Nikola Tesla advocated a change to AC power distribution. DC generators and motors were limited in voltage because of their arcing. Because of this low voltage, DC power distribution depended on many small generating stations. AC power permitted high voltage generation with distribution over long lines using step-up and step-down transformers. Edison briefly employed Tesla and a wage dispute helped to fuel their feud.

Nikola Tesla and George Westinghouse provided AC power for the Columbia Exposition in 1893, a spectacular success, and then harnessed Niagara Falls for AC power in 1895. When the state of New York used AC power for its electric chair, Edison promoted the view that AC was more dangerous than DC. His campaign was futile and he had to adapt his inventions to AC power. Ironically, Tesla received the Edison Medal in 1917 for his work in electricity.

Alternating Current Ammeter

General Electric manufactured this AC ammeter, but it carries the name of Elihu Thompson, the inventor of the Thomson-Rice DC ammeter. It was made about the same time as AC power distribution commenced.

The scale of this ammeter reads 0 to 500. Under the scale:

THOMPSON ALTERNATING AMMETER
NO. 297314 TYPE P
GENERAL ELECTRIC CO., U.S.A.

C. Trans.100:1 60 ~

The latest patent date on this ammeter is July 14, 1903. On the left is a button switch and two wire terminals on the right side. Mahogany base with brass cover. Height: 6 in. Width: 6 1/2 in.

This AC power tree supplanted many of the native species in our cities.

See "Direct Current Ammeter" and "Voltmeter."

Alternating current ammeter - same type, quality and period - 1997 - $112

69

Voltmeter

In the 18th century, the strange phenomena of magnetism and electricity were thought to somehow explain animal life. The claims of animal magnetism by Dr. Franz Anton Mesmer (1734-1815) inspired the popular novel, *Trilby,* about Svengali's sinister hypnotic influence over his lovely young protege. About the same time that Mesmer proposed the mystical hypnotic force of animal magnetism, Luigi Galvani (1737-1798) proposed animal electricity. Based on his experiments with frog muscles, Galvani claimed that electricity was produced by those muscles.

To Alessandro Volta (1745-1827), Galvani's claims seemed more mystical than scientific. So, he conducted a series of experiments showing that electricity was generated by a circuit containing two different metals immersed in a saline solution, and not by animal muscles. In doing so, Volta invented the first chemical voltaic cell or battery. That an eel could generate electricity would have shocked Alessandro Volta.

The volt, a unit measure of electromotive force, was named in Volta's honor for his scientific investigations. Voltage is analogous to electrical pressure. A volt is the unit of electromotive force needed to move one ampere through a resistance of one ohm.

The scale of this voltmeter reads from 0 to 600 volts A.C. The mirrored arc under the scale helps prevent parallax needle readings. If one is not looking dead on the needle, one sees a needle reflection on the arc. There are two terminals on the left side, a ground terminal is on the right side and a calibrating screw on the front. A button on the front turns the meter on when it is pressed.

Edward Weston (1850-1936) an English- American, developed the first accurate voltmeter and founded the Weston Electric Instrument Company. This brilliant inventor created the first portable lightmeter.

Walnut case with a leather strap handle on the top.

Height: 8 3/4 in. Width: 8 in. Depth: 4 in.

Manufacturer: Weston Electrical Instrument Corp.
Newark, N.J.

Patent dates: Jan. 1, 1895. Mar. 22, 1898.
Oct 4, 1898.

Model 155. Serial No. 67980.

A somewhat later version of the voltmeter.

See "Dirrect Current Ammeter" and "Alternating Current Ammeter."

Voltmeter - same type, quality and period - 2004 - $100

Testing Set

An English engineer's single-minded dedication to the Atlantic cable commenced a chain of events leading to the "Perdicaris Incident." This testing set includes a Varley loop circuit, used to locate breaks in power lines or cables. C.F. Varley invented this circuitry as Chief Electrical Engineer for the Atlantic cable, work that kept him on the high seas and away from his lovely wife, Ellen. In 1871, during Varley's prolonged absence, Ellen fell in love with Ion Perdicaris, a wealthy Greek-American.

After Ellen's divorce, Perdicaris took Ellen and her children to Morocco. While there in 1904, Perdicaris and Ellen's son were kidnapped by Raisuli, a bandit who demanded ransom from the Moroccan Sultan. Believing that American citizens had been kidnapped, the U.S. Secretary of State, John Hay, stated, "This governement wants Perdicaris alive or Raisuli dead." Theodore Roosevelt sent a fleet of battleships to the coast of Morocco to force the release of the victims. The Sultan paid the ransom and the victims were freed. That Roosevelt was precipitous and neither of the kidnap victims was a United States citizen was not revealed until 1933. Had Varley kept the home fires burning, there would never have been a Perdicaris Incident.

C.F. Varley had broad interests and shared curiosity about the occult with William Crookes, the physicist. Together they conducted experiments intended to measure psychic phenomena.

Varley's test to locate ground faults in power or communication lines is based on measurements in combination with the known resistance per unit length of the lines. This is a Peerless Switch Dial Testing Set T-2002. It is equipped for a Varley Loop Test and a Murray Loop Test for finding ground faults. It measures resistance and voltage. It was manufactured by the Thompson-Levering Company, Philadelphia, PA. SN 14948. Case width: 9 1/2 in. Case height: 5 3/4 in. Case depth: 6 in. To the right is a later version of this instrument.

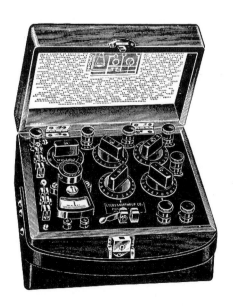

See "Oscillating Cylinder Steam Engine" and "Crookes Tube."

Telegraph Key

Slough, England, January 1, 1845. In celebration of the new year, Sarah Hart took a drink from her bottle of stout. Moments later she fell to the floor frothing at the mouth and died. She had been poisoned with prussic acid by her former lover, John Tawell.

A neighbor found Sarah, called the police and described the murderer as a man wearing the distinctive dress of a Quaker. John Tawell was a Quaker and had just been seen boarding a train to London. The police officer used the newly-installed Slough station telegraph to inform police in Paddington of the suspects description. Further down the line at Paddington, an officer boarded the train and John Tawell was arrested in London. He was hanged on March 28, 1845.

The telegraph had been used to apprehend a criminal. Sherlock Holmes could not have brought the felon to justice more quickly. The notorious crime and apprehension persuaded a skeptical public that the telegraph was not a mere novelty, but a practical means of communicating. The inventive genius and dedication of those who created the telegraph system, Charles Wheatstone, William Cooke and Samuel Morse, were recognized.

As early as 1773, experiments were underway with telegraphy when a system with 26 wires, one for each letter of the alphabet, was designed. Later experiments used the movement of an electrically-magnetized needle as the signal. The use of a simple key, sounder, relay, adequately insulated wires, and the Morse Code made telegraphy feasible for national and international communications.

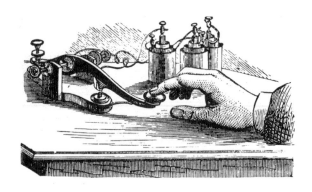

Except for the knob, this key is all brass and made by the Signal Electric Company of Menominee, Michigan. It was probably used with a wireless transmitter, rather than a land line. Thumbwheels with locking nuts adjust spring tension, extent of key movement, and centering of the key over contacts. The key dates from the first quarter of the 20th century. The Signal Electric Company was founded in 1892 and manufactured radio instruments, telegraph instruments, batteries and small electric motors. Signal Electric was acquired by King-Seeley Thermos Co. in 1952.

Overall length of key: 5 1/2 in. Width of base: 2 1/8 in.

Contemplating the telegraph provoked this profound insight from Albert Einstein: "You see, wire telegraph is a kind of very, very long cat. You pull his tail in New York and his head is meowing in Los Angeles. Do you understand this? And radio operates exactly the same way; you send signals here, they receive them there. The only difference is that there is no cat."

Telegraph key - same type, quality and period - 2004 - $45

Electric Motor

This electric motor is a diminutive example of the type that replaced mechanical power transmission towards the end of the 19th century. It operates on six-volt direct current. It has two brass thumbscrew terminals, spring-loaded brass carbon brush holders and exposed copper commutator. There are brass oil cups with caps at both ends of the shaft. The housing and base are heavy cast iron. It works either way one starts the rotation, clockwise or counterclockwise.

> Overall length: 6 1/2 in.
> Overall height: 6 in.
> Width of housing: 4 1/2 in.

Generally, early electrical equipment is free of ornamentation. Fortunately, designers knew too little about electricity to muck about with the functional engineering. Otherwise, we would have electric motors with Gothic arches or Greek columns, as some mid-19th-century steam engines were designed.

"You used my wedding dress for *what*?" A probable response of Mrs. Davenport when she learned that her husband, Thomas, had used her silk wedding dress to insulate wires in an electromagnet. Thomas Davenport (1802-1851), a Vermont blacksmith, invented the first practical electric motor with two fixed and two rotating electromagnets in 1834. His design is the basis of all subsequent rotating electric motors.

In the 19th-century factory, the factory hand worked under a canopy of pulleys, belts and shafts. These rattled, creaked and clanked as they delivered power from a central steam engine or water wheel to each work station. The genius of Thomas Davenport changed all that.

The electric motor could power tools individually, allowing a great deal more flexibility in factory design. Operating speed could be more easily adjusted for each tool. These advantages facilitated the modern assembly line as the electric motor displaced central mechanical power, belt pulleys and line shafts.

Here is a full-size relative as shown in *The Engineer,* 1904.

See "Belt Pulley" and "Electric Drill."

Electric motor - same type, quality and period - 2008 - $255

Electric Drill

In the 1830s, Thomas Davenport powered a drill press with the first electric motor, a motor of his own invention. It was the first use of an electric motor to power a tool. If you recall the movies *Brazil* and *Marathon Man*, then you recall the electric dental drill as an instrument of torture. We can thank George F. Green of Kalamazoo, Michigan, for its invention in 1875. We're more comfortable with an electric drill in the hands of a mechanic than in the hands of a dentist. Arthur James Arnot, an Australian, patented an electric drill for quarrying and mining in 1889. Adolph Pedersen of Cleveland, Ohio, patented a portable electric drill in 1906. Robert H. Riley invented the first cordless power drill in 1960. It was the precursor of all subsequent cordless power tools.

S. Duncan Black and Alonzo G. Decker founded Black & Decker Manufacturing Company in 1910 in a suburb of Baltimore, Maryland. Originally, the company manufactured highly-specialized industrial machinery. In 1916, it manufactured the first portable electric drill with a pistol grip and trigger switch. Some designs are so inspired that they become permanently integral with a specific function. Such is the case of the pistol grip and trigger switch for the electric hand drill. Aside from its convenience in its initial use, the pistol grip and trigger switch may have had some macho appeal. Now, this design is ubiquitous, used in everything from blowdryers to eggbeaters to spring-loaded fly swatters. What's next – a baby pacifier with pistol grip and trigger switch?

Length: 10 3/4 in. Height at handle: 4 3/4 in.

On brass maker's plate:

BLACK & DECKER
1/4 ELECTRIC DRILL
A.C. D.C. VOLTS AMPS
          110   1.7
R.P.M.   SERIAL NO.
1500   T11400
PATENTED NOV. 6, 1917

THE BLACK & DECKER MFG. CO.
BALTIMORE, MD. U.S.A.

WE ALSO MAKE THE FOLLOWING SIZES
5/16" 3/8" 1/2" 9/16" 5/8" 7/8" & 1 1/4"

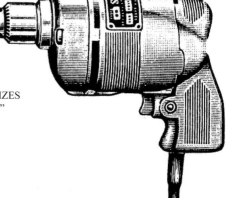

A mid 20th-century electric hand drill

See "Bitstock" and "Electric Motor."

Electric drill - same type, quality and period - 2005 - $12

Slide Projector or Magic Lantern

Athanasius Kircher showed the first illustration of the projector, magic lantern or sciopticon in one of his works in the late 17th century. Why was it called a "magic" lantern? For audiences unsophisticated in visual effects, their first view of projected images seemed a magical experience. Some shows were projections of ghostly images on moving gauze, a magical feature. Other-worldly images or "phantasmagoria" were standard fare of magic lantern shows. These images were made to vary in size and intensity to further amaze the viewers.

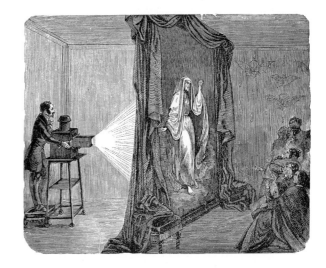

The earliest slides were painted images. Then lithographic images were used. These were succeeded by black and white positive photographic images and then hand-tinted photographic images. Panoramic slides were made in a long narrow format to show landscapes. Some slides had layers of moveable glass (kinetic slides), enabling the projectionist to show some limited movement of the image. In the Edwardian period, a popular English slide show was entitled, *What the Butler Saw,* rated for mature audiences only.

From front to rear of this projector: the focusing mechanism is brass, screwing into a cast aluminum conical housing attached to a large, wide, heavy brass cylinder, attached to a blued sheet steel and riveted cylindrical housing. The legs are cast aluminum. Construction is of quite high quality. The aluminum parts would have been uncommon at the turn of the century. The sheet steel is heavy and carefully assembled. The rack and pinion focusing has a movement of 1 1/8 in. The cherry slide bracket holds slides of 4 in. by 3 1/2 in. The light socket is adjustable in height, forward and back, on a brass base with position locking screws. The wood case is painted green and has reinforced sheet metal edges.

Turn the crank and the windmill spins.

With the advent of motion pictures in the late 1890's, followed by television and cinerama, the magic died and the magic lantern became a slide projector.

First quarter 20th century.
No makers' name.

Length: 17 1/2 in
Height: 11 1/4 in
Width of base: 7 in.

Magneto

Magneto, the superhuman mutant of the comics, has almost limitless power in manipulating any form of energy related to magnetism. He is a destructive, villainous enemy of both less endowed humans and the mutant X-men. In contrast, the conventional magneto, as a rugged, reliable and self-contained source of electric power, has greatly benefited human industry.

A magneto generates direct current through the rotation of a coil in the field of a permanent magnet. Michael Faraday (1791-1867), a British physicist and chemist, discovered electromagnetic induction and invented an experimental magneto. In the late 19th century, improvements in the magneto made it practical for ignition in internal combustion engines. Another early application was in hand-cranked ringing circuits for telephone systems. Currently, magnetos are used for ignition in many small engines, such as those powering gardening tools. Magnetos are also used in small motorcycles and small aircraft.

This magneto has two permanent horseshoe magnets astride a brass case and base. The case contains a rotating coil. Direct current is induced in the coil when it is rotated in the magnetic field by means of a friction-drive leather-rimmed wheel projecting from the back. It is somewhat unusual in its brass fittings.

This Perfection magneto is very similar to one manufactured by the Holtzer-Cabot Electric Company. The Company was founded in 1880 and headquartered in Boston. The company manufactured electric carriages in 1891. It also manufactured early telephone equipment and electric motors. It is possible that Holtzer-Cabot licensed the manufacture of this magneto to The Perfection Magneto Co.

Magneto dated to about 1905.

Height: 5 in. Width: 4 in. Length: 6 1/2 in.

On maker's brass plate: Made By The Perfection Magneto Co.
                        No. 2386
                        Rev. 2500
                        Anderson. Ind. U.S.A.

Holtzer-Cabot magneto

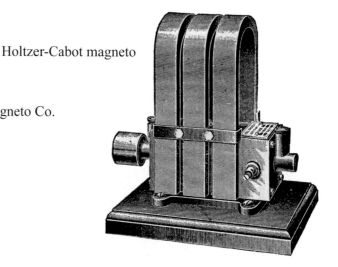

Magneto - same type, quality and period - 2005 - $50

Marine Searchlight

In the age of sonar, radar and GPS, searchlights still have a role in navigation. Captain Giles Kelly was steering the U.S. Presidential Yacht *Sequoia* in Galveston Bay. This 104-foot yacht was an historic relic and Kelly was mindful of his important charge. It was night and visibility was poor. The radar scope showed a line moving across the bow about 100 yards ahead. Binoculars proved useless so Kelly ordered the searchlights on. They revealed the *Sequoia* narrowly missing a mother duck trailing her ducklings - a close call.

In the early 19th century, Thomas Drummond invented the process of burning a gas with the flame concentrated on a lime block, causing the lime to ignite. The process produced an especially brilliant light (limelight) at the risk of occasional explosions. It was used primarily in theatre spotlights where one individual was illuminated to the exclusion of others. Hence, "in the limelight" or in the focus of public attention.

With the availability of electricity, carbon-arc light supplanted limelight. This searchlight originally used a carbon-arc light and was later modified for an incandescent light. It is brass with a copper back. A thumbwheel moves the light forward and back in front of a heavy parabolic mirror for focus. The front glass consists of glass strips to accommodate expansion due to heat.

Length: 14 1/2 in. Diameter at front: 9 1/2 in.

This is the manufacturer's brass plaque on the back of the spotlight.

The Carlisle & Finch Company of Cincinnati, Ohio, pioneered high-intensity carbon-arc technology. The Company manufactured searchlights in 1894 and is still a leading manufacturer of searchlights and lighthouse beacons. To the right is a searchlight viewed from the back and showing the carbon-arc mechanism.

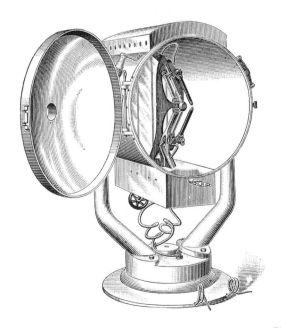

Temperature Potentiometer

Then was Nebuchadnezar full of fury, and the form of his visage was changed against Shadrach, Meshach and Abednego: therefore he spake, and commanded that they heat the furnace one seven times more than it was wont to be heated. And he commanded the most mighty men that were in his army to bind Shadrach, Meshach and Abednego, and to cast them into the burning fiery furnace.

To reliably increase the temperature seven fold, Nebuchadnezer would need to measure that temperature. This temperature potentiometer, a kind of thermometer, would have done the job for him. It was used in a heating system with more benign purposes than Nebchudnezer's, possibly in a refinery. It employs a thermocouple, a highly accurate sensor. A thermocouple produces a voltage proportional to the temperature to which it is exposed. In this device, that voltage is compared to the voltage in a circuit controlled by a potentiometer (a variable resistor). The potentiometer is linked to a dial with temperature readings. The dial is adjusted until the potentiometer circuit voltage matches the voltage of the thermocouple circuit when the meter at the top (a galvanometer) reads zero. Then, the temperature is read from the large potentiometer dial.

The thermocouple for this device is iron and constantan. Constantan is an alloy of copper and zinc. The temperature scale reads from 0° to 1,000° F.

The case is heavy cast brass and nickel-plated with a hinged front cover. Height from top of meter: 10 in. Width: 6 1/4 in. Depth: 3 3/4 in.

On front cover: PATENTED
             LEEDS & NORTHRUP CO.
             PHILADELPHIA

Serial number on cover: 104075. Dated to the first quarter of the 20th century.

Morris Evans Leeds founded Morris E. Leeds & Co. in 1899. In 1903, he joined with Edwin F. Northrup to form the Leeds & Northrup Co. in Philadelphia. Leeds invented a mercury cell to produce a reference voltage. This cell became the standard international voltage reference. Such a cell is incorporated in this temperature potentiometer. Leeds & Northrup manufactured a wide variety of electrical instruments including galvanometers, standard resistances, condensers, potentiometers, recording devices, electrochemical apparatus, controls and thermocouples.

To the left is a mid-20th century portable temperature potentiometer.

Radio Navigation Indicator

One of the strangest aviation incidents of World War II was the mysterious disappearance of a B-24 Liberator and its crew of nine. On its final flight, *Lady Be Good* was returning to a Libyan airfield, Soluch, from an aborted bombing raid on Naples on the night of April 4, 1943. Her last communication was a radio message to the Benina Direction Finder Radio Station in Libya shortly after midnight. The message stated that the aircraft's automatic direction finder was not working properly and requested a position report. There is no indication *Lady Be Good* received a response. She had vanished. Sixteen years later, on February 27, 1959, the wreckage of *Lady Be Good* was found by British oilmen in the Libyan desert about 400 miles south of its home base at Soluch. Bodies of eight of the crew were found. One crew member had walked 109 miles across the desert sand with little or no water.

Why did the aircraft fly 400 miles into the desert beyond its destination? A possible explanation is the problem of reciprocal bearings. In early radio direction finding, it was sometimes difficult to determine whether one was heading on a line towards or away from the radio source, 90° or its opposite bearing of 270°, for example. The navigation system of the B-24 Liberator included the same model of radio navigation indicator you see here.

This is an early combined VOR and ILS indicator. VOR stands for Very high frequency Omnidirectional Radio range and ILS stands for Instrument Landing System. VOR transmitting stations transmit two signals with a different phase relationship for each direction or radial from the transmitter. Later indicators identify specific radials. The vertical needle of this indicator, when centered, indicates only that the aircraft is on a radial to or from the transmitter. It does *not* show whether that radial is *either* to or from the transmitter as in later indicators. The ILS indicator, the horizontal needle, shows whether the aircraft is on (centered), above or below the proper landing slope as the aircraft approaches the airfield. In navigating, the pilot "follows the needle" to correct his position until the needle is centered. Left if the needle pointed left, or up if the needle pointed up, for example.

Before global positioning systems and accurate radio navigation systems, the navigator found an aircraft's location through *pilotage;* recognizing landmarks, *dead reckoning:* calculating distance and direction from one's last known geographic position; *celestial navigation*: determining location by reference to celestial bodies. These methods were often ineffective due to weather conditions, featureless landscapes or unreliable instruments. *Radio navigation* was in its earliest stages in 1943. Its reliability was not good enough for *Lady Be Good.*

This indicator was used in the B-17, B-24 and B-25 bombers of World War II. The back is stamped:

      S.C.U.S ARMY
      INDICATOR I-101 C

S.C.U.S. ARMY stands for Signal Corps U.S. Army.

Steel case. Diameter of face: 3 1/8 in. Depth: 2 3/4 in.

Radio navigation indicator - same type, quality and period - 2006 - $30

Electric Razor

George Bernard Shaw recounts this anecdote. As a child, he was watching his father shave and noted the nuisance it entailed. He asked his father why he shaved. His father stopped, thought a few moments, put down his razor and never shaved again. Shaw's own beard was as much of a hallmark as his Shavian wit.

In the 1930s the electric razor was an idea whose time had come. Siemens, Electro-Shave and Schick all introduced electric razors in this period. Saul Shaler of New York patented the Vibro-Shave electric razor in 1925. It had a solenoid and spring mechanism that vibrated a double-edged razor blade. The Vibro-Shave had a design very similar to this razor, also invented by Shaler. In 1932 he filed a patent for this single-edged, vibrating razor manufactured by the Tark Electric Razor Company of New York. It remained in production until 1938. Promotions showed the razor used with shaving cream. Considering its light insulation, anyone using this razor for a wet shave could find his razor burn accompanied by a 110-volt jolt.

An early electric razor, invented by Colonel Jacob Schick and first marketed in 1929, consisted of an electric motor connected to the shaver by a flexible shaft. The shaving head, a fine comb, held hairs while a reciprocating slotted blade cut them off. This first model was poorly received. He redesigned the shaver as a single unit in an enclosed bakelite case to be used with one hand and introduced it in 1931. It was an instant success and the Schick electric razor dominated the market for many years.

Philosophers used Occam's Razor for a metaphorical close shave. William of Occam, *Doctor Singularis et Invincibilis*, was a brilliant 13th-century English cleric and scholar. He vigorously debated the nature of civil and religious authority. He first stated the concept that all unnecessary facts or constituents in the subject being analyzed should be eliminated (as with a razor). Restated: where there are multiple explanations of the same phenomenon, the simplest consistent with the relevant facts should be accepted. This principle of economy in philosophical inquiry is known as Occam's Razor. Using it, one would choose the heliocentric over the geocentric theory of planetary movement, the molecular over the phlogiston theory of combustion and the omelette over the frittata.

Brass blade holder and hard rubber handle. Length: 4 3/4 in.

Manufacturer: Tark Electric Razor Co.

Stamped on ferrule: 110 volts 5 watts

Electric razor - same type, quality and period - 2006 - $30

Blasting Machine

It's a blast, especially with this machine. It is smaller and less threatening than the traditional large box with a plunger actuated mechanism used by Wile E. Coyote. Designed to fire up to ten charges at the same time, this blasting machine was used in mining, quarrying and road-building. It is basically a magneto and generates direct current with the twist of the handle. The current fires blasting caps seated in dynamite or blasting powder. As a safety feature, circuitry prevents the flow of electricity until sufficient current is generated to fire the caps.

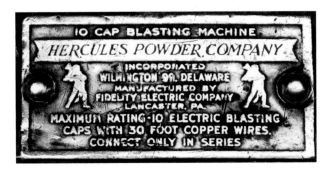

The Laflin & Rand Powder Co. was formed from a merger in 1869. In 1880 Laflin & Rand and Dupont founded the Hercules Powder Co. In 1902, Dupont purchased Laflin & Rand. Because of Dupont's monopolistic practices, it was forced to divest itself of the Hercules Powder Co. in 1912. The primary product of Hercules was smokeless powder.

The Hercules Powder Co. exploded into the headlines when, on September 12, 1940, 297,000 pounds of gunpowder blew up at its plant in Kenvil, New Jersey, killing 51 and wounding 200 persons. The blast was recorded on a seismograph at Fordham University, 50 miles away. Initially, sabotage was suspected, but the explosion was generally regarded as an industrial accident, one of a series of fatal explosions at the plant beginning in 1934.

Lead-coated brass case. Height including handle: 8 1/2 in.

Manufactured by: Fidelity Electric Company, Lancaster, PA for the Hercules Powder Company, Wilmington, Delaware

See "Magneto" and "Miner's Safety Lamp."

Blasting machine - same type, quality and period - 2006 - $190

Tabulating Machine

This tabulating machine is the genesis of IBM. Herman Hollereith (1860-1929) invented the punch card tabulator. The lever device is a punch card reader with pins that close circuits when they pass through holes in the card. The closed circuits move the counters shown above the reader. The system was first used for tabulating U.S. Army medical statistics and then for the U.S. census.

Electric Motors

The electric motor was a revolutionary invention and in the late 19th-century it took some unusual forms. Most used direct current. Here are a few examples and their distinguishing features.

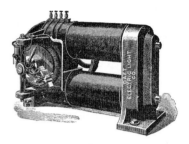

Daft Motor - 6 horsepower

Diehl Motor - variable speed

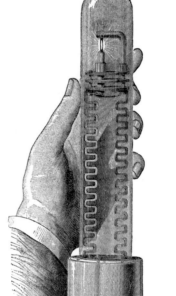

Electric Light Bulb

Before tungsten, early light bulbs had carbon filaments, as does this 1895 version. The zigzag conductors inside the bulb dissipated heat.

United States Motor - inexpensive winding

Rechniewski Motor - alternating current

Electric Fan

An electric fan manufactured by Crocker-Wheeler in about 1895. The blade diameter was 12 inches. This fan was used extensively in offices.

A few more examples of electrical technology

Dynamo

A dynamo with commutator generates direct current by rotating electromagnetic coils (wire coiled around a soft iron core) within the magnetic field of other electromagnetic coils. Michael Faraday invented this form of electricity generation and Ernst Werner von Siemens improved it in 1846.

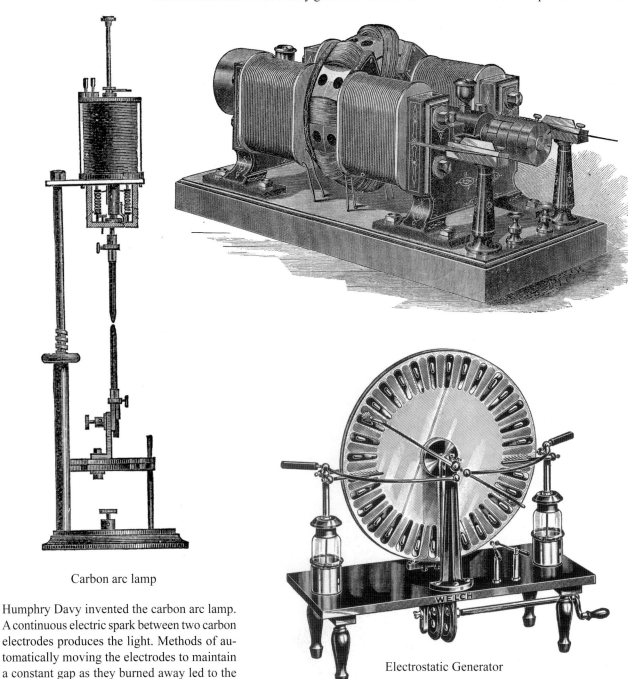

Carbon arc lamp

Humphry Davy invented the carbon arc lamp. A continuous electric spark between two carbon electrodes produces the light. Methods of automatically moving the electrodes to maintain a constant gap as they burned away led to the arc lamp's general use in street lighting beginning in 1879.

Electrostatic Generator

This type of generator was used for demonstration purposes. James Wimhurst invented it in 1881. It consists of two glass disks with metal segments spinning opposite to each other. Brushes contacting the metal segments pick up the static charge which is conducted to the Leyden jars. These temporarily store the charge until it is strong enough to jump the spark gap.

Electrical technology update

In 1980, nuclear energy generated 11% of electric power in the United States. In 1988, it generated 19% and that percentage has remained constant ever since. Because of the Three Mile Island accident and related concerns about nuclear safety, nuclear electrical generation has failed to fulfill its promise of cheap, safe and reliable electric power. The late 20th-century technological change with the most direct impact on our culture and society was not the production of electricity, but its *control*.

First developed in 1958 by Jack Kilby and Robert Noyce, the integrated circuit or microchip has superseded pre-existing control circuitry and has found thousands of applications where electronic circuitry had never been used before. A microchip includes circuitry etched on layered silicon wafers. A chip about one-quarter inch square may contain millions of transistors or other components. We have not, as yet, explored the full potential and versatility of the integrated circuit.

The digital function of integrated circuitry permitted extraordinary speed and precision in electronic processes compared to the analog function of conventional circuitry. Integrated circuitry vastly improved electronic reliability, economy and miniaturization. The microchip fueled the explosive growth of the computer industry. It replaced conventional circuitry in appliances and communication devices and greatly enhanced their usefulness. The microchip has affected virtually every aspect of our lives. Just a few new applications include:

Cellular phones	Electronic identification chips
Safety airbags	Digital cameras
Palm pilots	Media and information storage
Global positioning systems	Human anatomical replacements
Talking greeting cards	Video play stations
Mars Rovers	Robotics

Gordon Moore, a founder of Intel, predicted the progress of integrated circuits. He stated that at our rate of technological development, the complexity of integrated circuits or the number of transistors per chip relative to cost will double every 24 months. Known as Moore's Law, it has been enforced from 1971 to the present. At some point in the future, Moore's Law will be repealed as the diminishing size of transistors approaches atomic dimensions.

Moore also said, "If the auto industry advanced as rapidly as the semiconductor industry, a Rolls Royce would get a half million miles per gallon, and it would be cheaper to throw it away than to park it."

5 AWARDING THE DAEDALUS

Cylindrical slide rule
Mechanical calculator
Belt pulley
Speed indicator
Airplane propeller
Bevel gear casting pattern
Paper tester
Drafting set
Trammel points
Industrial thermometer
Standard roughness specimens
Spherometer
Water current meter
Anemometer
Self-recording thermometer

Here we are at the awards ceremony for the world's greatest engineer. That honor is symbolized by the presentation of a small bronze statue of Daedalus (the mythic Greek inventor). Who are the nominees for the Daedalus? May we have the envelopes, please? And the first nomination is:

Ictinius and Callicrates for the Parthenon in 438 B.C. (much applause). The style of Athena's temple is now familiar worldwide in temples of Mammon. Next...

Leonardo da Vinci for his 16th-century science-fiction vision of a helicopter, submarine and armored tank (applause). Let's hope Isaac Asimov is not as prophetic.

James Watt for his steam engines which powered the industrial revolution (much applause). It seems the industrial revolutionaries overthrew the water wheel for the sake of Wal Mart.

Washington Augustus Roebling for the Brooklyn Bridge in 1883 (modest applause). His cable network holds New York City together.

Wilbur and Orville Wright for the first heavier-than-air flying machine in 1903 (much applause). They were allowed to keep their keys in their pockets and shoes on their feet when boarding a plane.

Thomas Alva Edison for the phonograph, the incandescent light bulb and motion pictures (much applause). Everybody gets an Oscar except the inventor of the movies.

Rube Goldberg for complicated devices with trivial purposes (laughter).

And the winner is...

This section presents instruments used by engineers and some products of their work.

Engineering Technology Time Line

Approximate Year of Manufacture of Objects in this Chapter		Year of Significant Events
	250 B.C.	Archimedes' principles of simple machines
	1621	Slide rule invented
	1760	Cast iron cog wheel invented
	1798	Whitney's process of mass production
	1810	Tachometer invented
	1828	Differential gear invented
	1859	Internal combustion engine invented
Drafting set	1880	
Paper tester	1887	
Belt pulley	1890	
Spherometer	1890	
	1897	Worm gear invented
	1903	Wrights invent heavier-than-air aircraft
Speed indicator	1905	
Water current meter	1908	Assembly line invented
Bevel gear casting pattern	1910	
Airplane propeller	1915	
Mechanical calculator	1915	
Cylindrical slide rule	1920	
Industrial thermometer	1920	
Anemometer	1920	
Trammel points	1930	
Standard roughness specimens	1950	
	1974	Personal computer invented

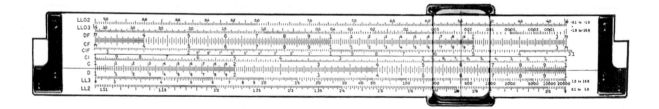

Cylindrical Slide Rule

The cylindrical slide rule, along with all other slide rules, has been superseded by the pocket calculator. Powered only by ambient light, the pocket calculator permitted older generations to forget the method of extracting square roots and concealed from younger generations that such a method ever existed.

The slide rule has its origins in John Napier's invention of logarithms. By using logarithms, multiplication and division is done by adding and subtracting exponents, vastly simplifying calculations. That John Napier (1550-1617) was an extraordinary genius was never a bone of contention. And that brings us to "Napier's bones", square bone or ivory rods with numerical tables on their sides invented by Napier to help with arithmetic calculations, a device that became very popular with European tradesmen and bookkeepers.

This English slide rule consists of nickel-plated brass cylinders wrapped with spiral logarithmic lines. The cylinders telescope. The cursor is a sliding sleeve with index marks at top and bottom rims that moves over both upper and lower scales. The rule has a leather case.

Professor George Fuller designed the first cylindrical slide rule in 1878. Its size of 3 1/2 in. by 17 in. permitted a spiral logarithmic line of 41 ft. 8 in. Small as it is, this Otis King slide rule has a logarithmic line of 66 inches, considerably longer than that of conventional slide rules. Overall length when opened: 11 in. Diameter: 1 1/4 in.

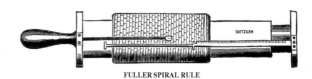

FULLER SPIRAL RULE

The top reads: MADE IN ENGLAND

The base of one scale reads:

PATENTEES & SOLE MANUFACTURERS:
CARBIC Ltd. 51 HOLBORN VIADUCT LODON EC1 (sic)
SCALE No. 429 COPYRIGHT

The base of a second scale reads: OTIS KING'S PATENT No. 187323

Not all engineers were enamored of the slide rule. Charles F. Kettering said, "When I was research head of General Motors and wanted a problem solved, I'd place a table outside the meeting room with a sign: LEAVE SLIDE RULES HERE! If I didn't do that, I'd find some engineer reaching for his slide rule. Then he'd be on his feet saying 'Boss, you can't do that.'"

Cylindrical slide rules - Same type, quality and period -
1996 $150
1999 $175
2003 $200
2006 $210

Mechanical Calculator

"It was near Thanksgiving Day 1884, and I decided to use the holiday in the construction of the wooden model. I went to the grocer's and selected a box which seemed to be about the right size for the casing. It was a macaroni box, so I have always called it the macaroni box model. For keys, I procured some meat skewers from the butcher around the corner and some staples from a hardware store for the key guides, and an assortment of elastic bands to be used for springs. When Thanksgiving Day came, I got home early and went to work with a few tools, principally a jackknife."

The inventor's first model of the Comptometer is in the collection of the Smithsonian Institute. Dorr Eugene Felt (1862-1939) makes its invention sound easy, but his first models were not developed for sale until 1887. The Comptometer was the first widely accepted mechanical calculator, antedating the printing calculator invented by William Seward Burroughs in 1891. Model A was produced in 1904 and about 6,000 of these were sold.

The great strength of this calculator was addition and subtraction, but multiplication, division and extracting square and cube roots could be performed by a skilled operator, and skilled operators were needed. Felt soon realized that the only way to assure growing machine sales was to assure available operators by training them. Eventually, about 150 Comptometer training centers were set up worldwide, constituting the largest private schooling system up to that time. Operators were primarily women and there was a ready market for their work. A Comptometer operator performed up to 200,000 keystrokes a day. Fingers were a blur on the keyboard.

Eugene Felt formed a partnership with Robert T. Tarrant in 1887 and the two incorporated in 1889 as the Felt & Tarrant Manufacturing Company of Chicago. Tarrant left the company in 1902. By 1930, the company had about 850 employees. In 1946, the company merged with the Victor Adding Machine Company. Mechanical calculators were supplanted by electronic versions in the 1960s.

This Model F Comptometer has a copper-plated sheet metal case with embossed filigree on the sides and a nickel-plated nameplate. Later models had the name "Comptometer" embossed on the front of the case.

Length: 14 in. Width: 9 1/4 in. Height: 5 1/4 in. including keys.

Latest patent date on case: Sept. 15, 1914. Serial number: 116579

Jonathan Swift describes computations well beyond the capacity of the Comptometer: "...it is reckoned, that there is not at present, a sufficient Quantity of new Matter left in Nature, to furnish and adorn any one particular Subject to the extent of a Volume. This I am told by a very skillful Computer, who hath given a full Demonstration of it from Rules of Arithmetick."

Mechanical calculator - same type, quality and period - 2006 - $132

Belt Pulley

Note the wooden pegs that hold the built-up pieces together and the spline in the rim.

On May 10, 1876 at the Centennial Exposition in Philadelphia, President Ulysses S. Grant threw a lever in Machinery Hall and the world's largest steam engine rumbled into motion. This steam engine was seventy feet high with a rating of 1,400 horsepower. It drove five miles of line shafts with flat belts and pulleys. As these shafts turned, lathes, cutters, saws, grinders, drills, planes, over a thousand machines, began to operate. On this day, the United States first flexed its industrial muscle before the world.

Up to the last quarter of the 19th century, power to factories was supplied by a central water wheel or steam engine. Power was distributed to work stations by elaborate systems of belt driven shafts and pulleys. In their complexity, these systems could rival the rigging of a clipper ship. Their design and installation was first the province of the millwright and then of the mechanical engineer.

The tool operator could start and stop his tool by using a "belt shipper" to shift the belt from the tool pulley to an idler pulley. Speed cones or stepped pulleys increased or decreased speed at different points in the power transmission. A disadvantage of these systems was energy loss due to friction and slippage, sometimes as much as a third of the energy input. An advantage was that the elasticity of the belts absorbed the shock of sudden changes in work load. Belt breakage and shaft misalignment were constant problems, sometimes posing a grave danger to workers. The flap of leather belting and the rumble of the shafts were the ubiquitous sounds of industry.

Most flat belt pulleys, such as this one, could be taken apart and assembled on a shaft without having to slide over the shaft end. The belt surface of this pulley is flat. Some pulleys are crowned, a feature that helped keep the belt centered on the pulley.

Wooden flat belt pulley. Diameter: 16 in. Rim width: 2 1/2 in.

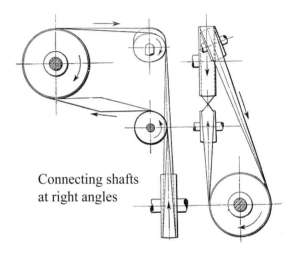

Connecting shafts at right angles

An iron flat belt pulley

See "Electric Motor" and "Speed Indicator."

Wooden flat belt pulley - same type, quality and period - 2004 - $40

Speed Indicator

A "speed indicator" is not a drug test. Here is an example application. A new milling machine was just installed on the shop floor, belted into the 19th-century pulley and shaft system, and there is chatter. It's not friendly chatter, but the sound of the milling cutter skipping over the workpiece and gouging it rather than making a smooth, even cut. The shop foreman uses his Starrett speed indicator and stop watch to find the cutter r.p.m. It's too fast, so he uses a smaller pulley to slow it down and the milling cutter stops its chatter.

Different machine tools have different optimum operating speeds. When machine tools were driven by pulley, belt and shaft power systems, the operating speed for each machine tool was adjusted by multiple pulleys or speed cones to step up or step down speed from the line shaft. The speed indicator was useful in making these adjustments. The speed indicator is actually a revolution counter. The count must be timed with a stop watch to find speed. To count revolutions of a shaft, one of several exchangeable rubber tips is held against the end of the shaft at its center.

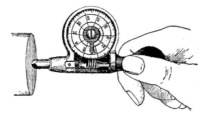

Speed indicators were replaced by tachometers that gave a direct r.p.m. reading. Tachometers were made obsolete for many purposes when 60 cycle per second alternating current became the standard reference for controlling speed in machine tools driven by electric motors.

This is a model No. 107 Starrett speed indicator. It counts revolutions up to 5,000. It has a hard rubber handle. It is nickel-plated steel and six inches in length.

L. S. Starrett (1836-1922) founded his Company in Athol, Massachusetts, in 1880. His motive was altruistic according to his statement, "I have believed that I could do no greater good than help create a business that would give people employment and a chance to earn an honest living." The L. S. Starrett Company still operates as a precision tool company. It manufactures micrometers, calipers, rules, tape measures, dial indicators and gauge blocks among other tools and measuring devices.

Engineer and Steam Engineering 1905

See "Universal Bevel Protractor" and "Revolution Counter."   Speed indicator - same type, quality and period - 2004 - $25

Airplane Propeller

At eight feet, this is a relatively large wooden propeller, though it is shorter than the Wright brothers' first propeller by six inches. The Wrights' propeller was carved from a single block of wood and turned at 350 r.p.m. This one is laminated. Modern wood propellers are shorter, narrower and thinner than this one and designed to turn at much higher speeds. Cross sections of a roughly similar wood propeller are shown here.

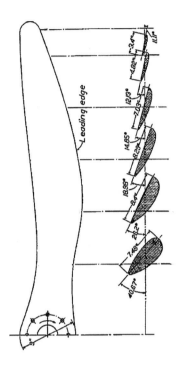

These blade cross sections may well remind you of wing cross sections. That the propeller was, essentially, a rotating wing was an explicit aerodynamics insight of the Wright brothers.

The propeller converts the rotating force of the engine into thrust. Thrust equals the mass of the air forced backwards by the propeller per second times the velocity added to this air.

Wood-laminated propeller with copper sheathed tips. Six laminations.
Stamped near hub: No. 958
Length: 8 ft.
Width at widest point: 9 1/2 in.
Thickness at hub: 4 in.

You may recall Antonioni's 1966 movie, *Blowup*. A very similar propeller was treasured by the passive hero, a photographer.

Could the propeller reduce global warming? From 5,000 B.C. in Babylon, windmills ground grain and pumped water. In the mid-20th century, very large wind turbines generated electricity with greatly improved efficiency. The aerodynamics of aircraft propeller design found direct application in these turbines. Instead of the turning propeller moving air, moving air turned the propeller-shaped turbine. Energy technologists predict that environmentally-friendly wind turbines will generate 12 percent of Europe's electric power by the year 2020.

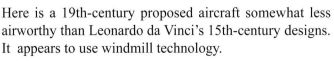

Here is a 19th-century proposed aircraft somewhat less airworthy than Leonardo da Vinci's 15th-century designs. It appears to use windmill technology.

Bevel Gear Casting Pattern

Forget technology. This work of art, this beautiful wooden sculpture, has no practical purpose. Its shape is complex and regular. There is a visual rhythm to the changing circumference and angled rays. Radiating lines and concentric circles suggest abstracts of nature: the sun, segmented fruit, a dandelion flower, transient circles in the water. Imagine this sculpture slowly turning in the light, producing alternating stripes of bright and shadow, an accelerated version of night and day.

The artist was skilled at woodwork and shows a profound sense of the geometrical. Perhaps he or she was influenced by Léger.

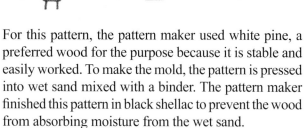

A casting pattern is used to create a mold into which molten metal is poured to produce a casting. This is a pattern for a bevel gear. Drive shafts that turn corners need bevel gears.

For this pattern, the pattern maker used white pine, a preferred wood for the purpose because it is stable and easily worked. To make the mold, the pattern is pressed into wet sand mixed with a binder. The pattern maker finished this pattern in black shellac to prevent the wood from absorbing moisture from the wet sand.

This pattern tells a lot about the final product. Cast iron is 16 times heavier than white pine. This pattern weighs 21 ounces, so the finished cast iron bevel gear weighs 21 pounds. Here you see the foundry pattern number (100026-B-45) in raised letters on a lead strip as part of this pattern. That number would appear as indented letters in the mold and as raised letters on the finished bevel gear casting.

The teeth on the pattern are straight, so the finished bevel gear rotated at less than about 500 rpm. For a gear of this size, mean circumference - 24 in., other tooth shapes are required at faster speeds. Because of the center angle of this gear pattern, 30 degrees, the finished gear was probably the pinion or smaller gear in a right angle combination.

Small diameter: 4 in.
Large diameter: 9 in.

"To fettle" is to clean up or place in order. The verb has a specific meaning for casting. It means to remove or polish away mold marks from the casting. A casting so polished would be in a "fine fettle"

See "Pattern Makers Sculpting Tools."

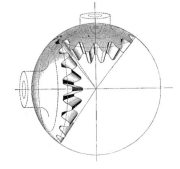

Theoretical model of bevel gears as parts of a sphere

Paper Tester

As you walk up the steps with the groceries, you wonder if the checker really should have put 10 cans of soup, 5 pounds of sugar, a gallon of milk and a dozen eggs all in the same bag. Then, you hear an ominous tearing sound. Kraft paper is used in the familiar grocery store brown paper bags. The word "kraft" is German for strength. At one time or another, after picking up cans and cleaning up eggs, you may have felt that kraft paper was not strong enough.

The bursting strength of kraft paper or any paper up to .025 in. thick is found by the standard Mullen test. B.F.Perkins and Son, Inc. is still manufacturing a version of this paper tester. This device forces an oil-filled diaphragm against the paper until the paper ruptures. The bursting strength of kraft paper in a grocery bag ranges from 28 to 47 pounds per square inch. Whether your grocery bag actually breaks depends a lot on how evenly the weight is distributed and how the checker packed it. Good Luck!

The original bag lady was Margaret E. Knight. In 1867, she devised the paper bag with a square bottom and invented the machinery to manufacture it. Her design became the standard grocery bag that stands up by itself as it is packed.

This paper tester has a black enameled cast iron frame, base and handwheel with hand-painted floral ornamentation. The frame and decoration remind one of a sewing machine. Some parts are nickel-plated. There is a brass edge-milled table on which the paper is clamped. The brass pressure gauge has a dial calibrated from 0 to 160 (pounds per square inch). Height: 12 1/4 in. Length: 16 in.

About 1887

Gauge dial reads:

> The Mullen Paper Tester
> Manf'd by
> B.F. Perkins & Son,
> Holyoke, Mass.
> U.S.A.

> Crosby Steam Gage
> & Valve Co.
> Boston
> 394   502

Frame reads:

> The Mullen Tester (front)
> Patented Feb. 22, 1887 (back)

Base reads:

> M'fg. by B.F. Perkins & Son

Paper tester - same type, quality and period -
1977 $8
2003 $117

Drafting Set

"Architect, n. One who drafts a plan of your house, and plans a draft of your money."
Ambrose Bierce, *The Devil's Dictionary*

The compass and straight edge were illustrated in Egyptian tomb decorations of 4000 B.C. The earliest engineering drawings are from the 16th century. In 1284, the great cathedral in Beauvais, France, collapsed disastrously. Just imagine the architect's legal liability exposure without the defense of working drawings.

In the late 20th century, the personal computer made the drafting set as obsolete as the slide rule. CAD (computer assisted design) has displaced these carefully crafted instruments and most of the draftsmen who used them. The 14 instruments in this set are made of steel, ivory, brass and german silver. German silver is an alloy of copper, nickel and zinc. The set was manufactured in about 1880. It includes the proportional dividers, compass and pen shown on the left. The case is rosewood veneered mahogany with a green velvet lining. The set is of Swiss or German manufacture. The dotting pen below (not part of the set) is rolled along the edge of a ruler to produce dotted or dashed lines according to the cam selected.

Beautifully executed architectural and mechanical drawings can be works of art in themselves. Their creators used these instruments, fine tools that evoke the fading profession of the accomplished draftsman.

Drafting set - same type, quality and period - 2003 $225

Trammel Points

"Trammel" means to entangle, restrain or confine as in "My heart is trammeled by my love's tresses." Generally, the word has a poetical usage, though a poetical engineer might say, "The part was trammeled by tensile stresses."

Trammel points are used to transfer dimensions or draw circles and arcs larger than can be done with dividers or a compass. The point holders slide along a beam and are fixed in place with clamping thumbscrews. One of the points is on a spring-loaded pivot for fine adjustments. A point can be unscrewed and the knurled pencil holder screwed in its place. Strictly speaking, the points and their holders are trammel points. The trammel points and beam assembly together are a beam compass. As with a compass, trammel points are used to generate hexagons, octagons and to divide angles. With it, figures are laid out in a drawing or directly on a workpiece for cuts. For drafting, the beam compass is another instrument superseded by Computer Assisted Design.

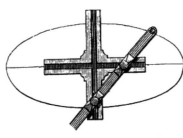 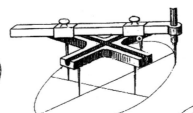

With an ellipsograph, a grooved cross, a beam compass can be used to draw ovals as shown here.

An engineering application of this ellipsograph concept of constraining grooves is the trammel wheel. One form is a circular plate with two or more cross grooves intersecting at the center. The smaller wheel with three rollers, not in line with the shaft of the larger wheel, transmits rotary motion to the larger grooved wheel.

This beam compass has two trammel points and a pencil holder. The hardware is nickel-plated brass. The beam is rosewood and 24 in. long. Early 20th century.

Stamping: The L.S. Starrett Co.
Athol, Mass. U.S.A.
No. 50-A.

19th-century trammel points.

See "Speed Indicator" about Starrett.

Trammel points - same type, quality and period - 2006 - $33

Industrial Thermometer

The temperature of the big bang: 1,000,000,000,000° K. The universe has been cooling off for the last 14 billion years. A law of thermodynamics states that heat, the vibration of molecules, flows only from warm matter to cooler matter. In theory, when all matter is at the same temperature, the universe will be in a state of entropy and no work can be done — a condition already reached in Congress.

The earliest thermometers date from about 1600. Since they lacked a standard scale or calibration, readings were not comparable. This was a real problem for more than a century.

"Bill, what temperature does your thermometer read?"

"Mine says 92. And yours?"

"It says 23. What about yours, Joe?"

"It says 76. Maybe we should just average them."

About 1714, Daniel Fahrenheit invented the sealed column mercury thermometer. He was the first to use the boiling point of water (212°) and freezing point of water (32°) as fundamental scale references. On early thermometers with Fahrenheit scales, normal body temperature was indicated as "blood heat", the temperature of the armpits of a healthy man. Other temperature scales include Celsius (0° = melting point of ice and 100° = boiling point of water), Kelvin (same degree intervals as Celsius, but 0° = absolute 0), Rankine and Réaumur.

This glass mercury industrial thermometer was used to measure the temperature of gases, vapors or liquids in monitoring industrial processes. Because of increasing recognition of mercury as a poison and environmental pollutant, alcohol and electronic thermometers are replacing mercury thermometers.

The manufacturer, Precision Thermometer & Instrument Company of Philadelphia, Pennsylvania, was founded in 1910 and eventually changed its name to Princo Instruments, Inc. The company also manufactured barometers and telegraph keys. The company is still in business and manufacturers industrial measurement and control devices.

Mercury glass thermometer reads: 0° to 220° F. A 9 1/2 -inch sensing stem projects from the back. Bronze case.

Height: 13 1/2 in. Width: 2 3/4 in. Depth: 1 1/4 in.

See "Temperature Potentiometer" and "Dough Thermometer."

Thermometer - same type, quality and period - 2005 - $60

Standard Roughness Specimens

"Rough and ready" describes things that are crudely formed or manufactured, but serviceable, usually with unfinished marks of production. Unnecessary roughness concerns the football umpire, the designer and the engineer. Marks of production may or may not be acceptable. To make the rough places plain without divine intervention, the engineer or designer specifies the desired degree of roughness or surface finish. He could refer to a set of samples such as those shown here. This kit contains 25 samples of metal surfaces with varying roughness resulting from one or more of these industrial processes:

burnishing	honing	sand casting
drawing	lapping	sawing
filing	milling	shaping
forging	precision casting	shearing
grinding	rolling	turning

Roughness specimens as finish guides have been generally superseded by surface roughness measuring instruments such as profilometers and interferometers. Using a profilometer, a stylus is drawn across a surface and its resulting movements are electronically amplified and digitalized. The most common reading is a center line average of peaks and valleys. On engineering drawings the average roughness can be specified in millionths of an inch or millionths of a meter using this symbol, suggesting a valley and a peak:

Ten cased pieces with 25 specimen finishes. Each piece 2 1/2 in. by 2 in.

Specimens manufactured by Micrometal Mfg. Co. of Ann Arbor, Michigan and developed by General Electric Co. of Schenectady, New York.

Standard roughness specimens - same type, quality and period - 2006 - $35

Spherometer

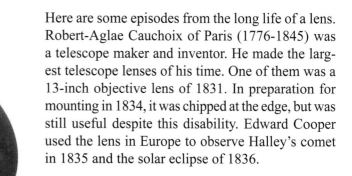

Here are some episodes from the long life of a lens. Robert-Aglae Cauchoix of Paris (1776-1845) was a telescope maker and inventor. He made the largest telescope lenses of his time. One of them was a 13-inch objective lens of 1831. In preparation for mounting in 1834, it was chipped at the edge, but was still useful despite this disability. Edward Cooper used the lens in Europe to observe Halley's comet in 1835 and the solar eclipse of 1836.

Another astronomer, Andrew Graham, used the telescope and Cauchoix's lens in cataloging the positions of 660,155 stars. About 1928, the lens was sold to a Jesuit Seminary in Hong Kong. The Jesuit observatory was bombed in 1941, but the telescope and lens were saved and moved to Manila in 1947. There, after 158 years, the lens found employment in solar spectography as late as 1989. A lens with such a distinguished career deserves its own name. How about the "Magnificent Eye" or in deference to its French origin, *L'Oeil Magnifique?*

In making the Magnificent Eye, Cauchoix certainly used his invention, the spherometer he designed in 1810. The spherometer measures regular curved surfaces, primarily lenses. Cauchoix's design of three legs with a central micrometer screw has remained essentially the same for mechanical spherometers to this day. The Conservatorie National des Arts et Metiers in Paris has a spherometer of Cauchoix's that reads to one thousandth of a millimeter.

A spherometer finds the radius of a regular curved surface or a sphere. It also measures the thickness of small, thin materials. Mechanical spherometers, such as this one, have three equidistant feet on points or small spheres and a central micrometer screw. After the height of the micrometer screw point is leveled with the three feet on a flat plane, the height of the micrometer screw is adjusted so that all four points contact the surface to be measured. This surface may be convex or concave. One can read the number of turns from the vertical scale and fractions of a single turn from the dial attached to the micrometer screw to measure the height of the micrometer screw relative to the feet. To calculate the radius R, the flat-plane distance between a foot point and the micrometer screw d and the height of the micrometer screw h are used in this equation: $R = (d^2 + 3h^2)/6h$.

This spherometer has a compound lever-actuated pointer that meets a calibration line when the micrometer screw correctly contacts a surface. The feet points screw into the base and there is a set of four holes in each leg of the base to span spherical surfaces of very different radii. It dates to the end of the 19th century. The base and legs are cast iron and the dial and scales are brass. Diameter of disk: 4 in. Divisions of disk: 200. Maximum horizontal distance between one foot point and the micrometer screw point: 5 in.

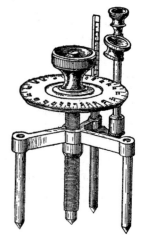

A very large spherometer applied to the Earth would show that it is not a sphere. It is a spheroid, a flattened sphere. The Earth's diameter at the equator is 17 miles greater than its diameter from pole to pole.

Spherometer - same type, quality and period - 2006 - $85

Water Current Meter

"Much water flows while the miller sleeps." "A mill cannot grind with water that is passed." These proverbs advise you to seize the moment; do it now. They derive from a time when flowing water was a vital source of power.

Even during the age of steam, water wheels and turbines powered many New England factories. Locating sites for these power sources was a critical decision. Suppose you wished to locate a water wheel on a stream. To find the maximum capacity for that water wheel, you need to know the maximum volume of water available. To find that volume, you need to know the velocity of the stream. You could use this water current meter to find that velocity.

The meter stem screws into a staff held or fixed under water. The bladed wheel drives an enclosed revolution counter started and stopped by a lever attached to a cord extending to the water surface. The revolution count is timed. An accompanying calibration certificate by the Department of the Interior, United States Geological Survey, Division of Hydrography, is dated April 2, 1908. One hundred forty calibration measurements for this particular instrument relate revolutions per second to velocity in feet per second.

The meter is made of nickel-plated brass.
Overall height: 10 in. Diameter of bladed wheel: 3 1/2 in.

Engraved on the meter: Buff & Buff Mfg. Co.
Boston, U.S.A.
3842

Founded in 1898, the Buff & Buff Manufacturing Company succeeded the firm of Buff & Berger. Buff & Buff, located in Boston, was a prominent maker of exceptionally fine surveying, engineering and scientific instruments. Curiously, eyepiece cross hairs in these instruments were made of spider web filaments from spiders collected under Boston bridges. Such filaments have tremendous strength, as Spiderman can testify.

For antique technology buffs, Buff & Buff instruments are prized.

A 19th-century factory water wheel with gearing

Water current meter - same type, quality and period - $147

Anemometer

The engraving shows an anemometer of a later design in which the air flow is not impeded by the dial.

Large anemometers or wind meters measure air speed for weather monitoring. This small anemometer usually measured air speeds in mines, tunnels, and in other applications for engineering purposes.

The Wright brothers used a small handheld anemometer of French manufacture for their measurements at Kitty Hawk. This anemometer was lent to them by Octave Chanute, another experimenter in early flight. The anemometer and stopwatch were attached to a strut of the Wright's flyer. They began recording when the flyer was released from a catch. Air speed over the wings was derived from the flight time and anemometer reading (number of wind vane revolutions). This data was used by the Wrights to determine lift and drag of the wings. Competitors at model airplane meets find wind speed with handheld anemometers.

Small anemometers served as the focus of an artistic event. In March of 2007, artist Patrick Marold deployed 2,700 modified anemometers on a mountainside at Vail, Colorado. The "windmill" project costs $94,000 and drew attention to this ski resort. These anemometers power lights that glow when wind speeds reach 15 miles per hour. The caprice of winds or the god Aeolus control the display. Fortunately, surface wind speeds never approached the maximum recorded on Mt. Washington, New Hampshire, of 231 miles per hour.

Although labeled "Keuffel & Esser", the unusual six-dial design of this anemometer indicates it was made for Keuffel & Esser of New York in the late 19th century by Robson, a British firm. The large counter dial measures to 100 feet (revolutions). The smaller dials measure hundreds, thousands, tens of thousands, hundreds of thousands and millions of feet. Wind speed in feet per minute would be calculated from a timed reading of the vane revolutions from the counter dials. The anemometer's overall height is 3 1/2 in. The diameter of the wind vanes is 2 3/4 in. It has a dial lock. Its serial number is 530.

See "Airplane Propeller."

Anemometer - same type, quality and period - 2009 - $256

Self-Recording Thermometer

Navigate with a thermometer? Benjamin Franklin proposed it and America's first meteorologist endorsed it. The Gulf Stream along our East Coast moves northward at a rate of about six miles per hour with a winter temperature off the coast of Florida of about 77 degrees F., considerably warmer than the rest of the Atlantic. If you want to stay on course while crossing the Gulf Stream, about 60 miles wide, you must compensate for the northward drift. Before GPS, you could tell when you were in the stream by measuring its temperature, a practice advocated by Daniel Draper, America's first meteorologist.

Daniel Draper (1841-1931) invented this self-recording thermometer. It recorded the temperature of the weather or the temperature of storage areas for perishables for a full week. Draper pursued a scientific career and became a meteorologist at a time when scientific concepts were first used in the study of weather. He was the official meteorologist of New York City and founded the New York Meteorological Observatory in Central Park. Among his other inventions were self-recording instruments to measure barometric pressure and rainfall. He set up the Draper Manufacturing Company to produce these instruments.

In this recording thermometer, a bi-metallic strip bends according to the temperature and levers amplify this movement to control the pen. The pen graphs the temperature on the rotating paper disk, driven by a pendulum clockwork.

Manufactured by the Draper Manufacturing Company of New York, N.Y. The latest patent date is 1887. The case is cast iron. Height: 14 in. Width: 10 1/2 in. Depth: 4 in.

See "Bathythermograph."

Self-recording thermometer - same type, quality and period - 2009 - $38

Below, Draper's patent drawings for the recording thermometer.

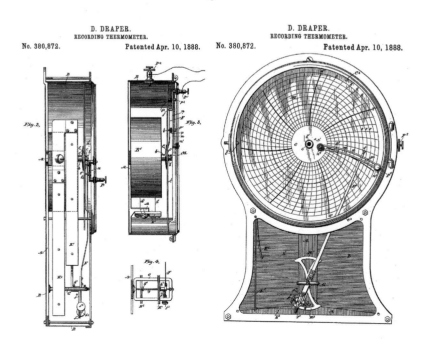

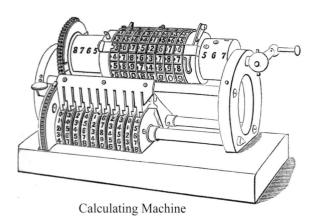

Calculating Machine

George Grant's calculator of the late 19th century. This is one of many designs based on rotating cylinders. This machine could be used for operations no more complicated than multiplication and division. See "Mechanical Calculator."

Pantograph

Based on the parallelogram and used in drafting to copy or to scale a drawing or map up or down. Invented in 1603. A more accurate and complex version, the eidograph, was invented by William Wallace in 1831.

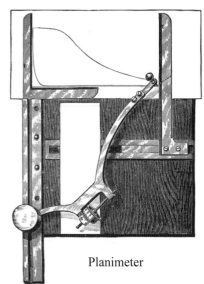

Planimeter

The planimeter is used to find the efficiency of both steam and internal combustion engines. It measures the area of indicator diagrams recording engine performance. See "Planimeter" and "Steam Engine Indicator."

Amsler's Recording Dynometer

In Amsler's dynometer, torque is transmitted through the levers to the springs. Their extent of compression is recorded on a paper tape moved by ratchet-driven drums at the top.

Mathematical Solids

A collection of solid shapes used as models to develop skill in drafting and engineering drawing. Not as curvilinear as your typical artist's model.

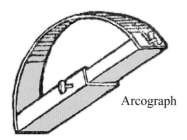

Arcograph

A strip of flexible spring steel used for drawing curves, serving a function similar to a spline.

A few more examples of engineering technology

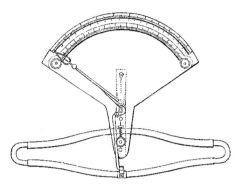

Dynometer

Used to measure torque or the force needed to pull or move a burden. The name derives from the "dyne", a metric unit of force. There are many special-purpose dynometers. Here, force is measured by means of linkage to both ends of the elliptical spring.

Gunter's Slide Rule

Gunter's scale or rule is a precursor of the logarithmic slide rule and includes logarithms, sines, tangents and other scales. Invented by Edmund Gunter (1581-1626). See "Cylindrical Slide Rule" and "Surveyor's Chain."

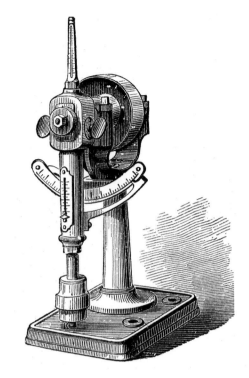

Lubricant Tester

This is Thurston's oil-testing machine of about 1877. The tester provides data for measuring the coeffficient of friction. Different lubricants and pressures are used on its bearing surfaces which support a pendulum, scales and thermometer. Depending on the properties of the lubricant, rotating the bearing surface at a constant speed would move the pendulum to different readings on the scale. See "Sight Feed Lubricator."

Spline

Used to draw smoothly curving lines other than circles or circle segments. A drafting tool used especially by naval architects. The weights are referred to as "ducks." Hence, "get your ducks in a row."

Caliper Testing Gauge

This gauge, suggestive of an armadillo, is composed of independently ground rings increasing in sizes of 1/16th inch and 1/8th inch increments to 2 1/2 inches. It is used to check the accuracy of fixed gauges and calipers. Made by the Standard Gauge and Tool Works of Philadelphia in the late 19th century.

Engineering technology update

For centuries, the engineer's practice relied on drafting pens, slide rules, and handbooks. All were replaced by the computer. The first to go was the drafting pen, T square and drawing board. CAD is an acronym for computer assisted design and computer assisted drafting. The core capability of CAD is converting graphic design concepts into working drawings. Output may also include three dimensional representations, specifications, bills of materials, and machining control codes to manufacture prototypes. The software includes symbol libraries, drawing conventions and engineering calculations customized for different engineering specializations. Some CAD functions overlap those of computer aided engineering (CAE).

For engineering problems BC (before computers), the solution was simple; build a prototype and see if it works. Not only was this solution simple, it was costly, time-consuming, often unreliable and sometimes dangerous. Computer aided engineering (CAE) supplanted the slide rule and converted the engineering handbook into a software manual. CAE generates representations of parts whose shapes or structures are then optimized through computation to resist stresses and assure functional compatibility with other parts. CAE software verifies designs according to design constraints and extensively models and simulates designs to anticipate and prevent failures. CAE simulates complicated mechanical, fluid and thermal systems. In all of these functions, engineering software replaces engineering hardware.

Computer aided manufacturing (CAM) instructions control tool paths and operations, move parts through processes and control raw materials and final product inventories. An advantage of CAM is greater machining precision than is possible with manual control. Another advantage is rapid and inexpensive set up, design change and modification of operations, a tremendous advantage in small batch and custom manufacturing. CAM software may even reorder production materials.

As a novel application of computerized engineering, consider the raising of the Confederate Civil War submarine, *H. L. Hunley.* She sank off the coast of Charleston in 1864 and was discovered in 1995. The *Hunley* was 40 feet long, weighed 65,000 pounds and had a diameter of four feet. After 136 years in silt, sand and salt water, rust and corrosion had severely weakened the vessel's plates and supporting structure. Any accident in raising the Hunley threatened the loss of this historical treasure. Extensive tests and surveys of the hull and its iron plates provided input for computer models replicating the hull and its properties. Then, computerized simulations of different support and lifting methods tested stress on the hull. Simulations showed the optimum method was to construct a rigid support frame over the *Hunley*, cushion the hull with large bags filled with foam conforming to its shape and suspend the submarine from the frame with 32 nylon slings. During the raising, computers monitored all structural loads to compensate for both weather and sea conditions. The project was completed successfully in October, 2000.

6 FRONTIERS OF KNOWLEDGE

Alembec
Hydrometer
Analytical balance
Barograph
Testing sieves
Incremental core sampler
Microscope
Spectroscope
Flash point tester
Crookes tube
Phrenological bust

What with the elimination of polio, landing a man on the moon, and the success of hair plugs, we have come to expect a lot of science. But, these tangible results are not the goal of science. They are incidental to the arrangement of facts to show the operation of general laws. They are by-products of the pursuit of knowledge. This section deals with some of the tools and instruments used in that pursuit.

There is a curious parallel in the social histories of art and science. In the 18th and early 19th centuries, the patrons of art and the patrons of science had a common motive. They wished to be memorialized in the works of those who were artistically and scientifically creative. Scientific instrument makers benefited from this motive. When science was faddish for the wealthy and aristocratic, a form of science chic, they purchased finely crafted telescopes, microscopes and celestial globes to ornament their drawing rooms. This trickle-down research funding subsidized, in part, the design of instruments for committed scientific scholars.

Now, scientific instruments have become much more expensive. With a price tag upwards of 50 million dollars for a cyclotron, the fashionable funding of science has lost its appeal.

Scientific Technology Time Line

Approximate Year of Manufacture of Objects in this Chapter		Year of Significant Events
	1590	Compound microscope invented
	1687	Newton's laws of gravitation and motion
	1643	Barometer invented
	1814	Spectroscope invented
Microscope	1850	
	1859	Darwin publishes theory of evolution
Phrenological bust	1865	Mendel's theory of genetics
Analytical balance	1890	
Hydrometer	1894	
Pocket spectroscope	1895	X-ray tube invented
Testing sieves	1907	Radioactive dating invented
Alembec	1910	
Barograph	1910	
	1916	Einstein's general theory of relativity
Flash point tester	1917	
Crookes tube	1920	
Incremental core sampler	1930	Cyclotron invented
	1932	Electron microscope invented
	1942	First self-sustaining nuclear fission
	1953	DNA discovered
	1968	Man on the moon
	1991	Controlled nuclear fusion

Alembic or Still

An alembic was familiar apparatus in the alchemist's workshop. Medieval alchemists believed that the physical world was made up of combinations of four essences: earth, fire, air and water. Some believed in a fifth essence, the quintessence. If sufficiently purified, this quintessence could bestow permanent health and even immortality. Many alchemists sought this quintessence through serial distillations of different substances. Their research may have produced *aqua vitae,* the water of life, but no cure for death.

Among the products of distillation are pure water, aromatic oils and gasoline. Perhaps, alcohol is the most interesting. "Alcohol", "alembic" and "alchemist" derive from the Arabic language. Distillation to produce alcoholic beverages may have been invented by the Arabs. Distillation began in Europe in the 12th century when wine was distilled to make brandy.

This brandy, originally used for medicinal purposes, was flavored with herbs and spices to disguise its bad taste. Flavored brandy evolved into liqueurs such as Benedictine and Chartreuse. While alcohol was prescribed to Christians, it was proscribed for devout Muslims. Some names of alcoholic spirits reflect their origin in fire and distillation. *Aqua ardens* for burning water. The Dutch *brantwijn* or burnt wine became "brandy." Then, there is the familiar American term, "fire water,"referring to either the taste or the origin.

The still on the right is a conventional working alcohol still. The still beneath it is a glass laboratory still. Within the condenser, you can see the coiled tube through which the distillate flows and is cooled, called a "worm."

The still at the top of the page is a copper laboratory still on brass legs. The retort and condenser lining are tinned. The retort lid has three brass wing nuts to screw down the lid to swiveling bolts on the retort itself.

This still is from the first quarter of the 20th century

Height of condenser: 13 1/4 in.
Diameter of condenser: 4 in.
Height of retort: 10 1/2 in.
Diameter of retort: 4 in.

Markings on rim of lid: 5

"Claret is the liquor for boys; port, for men; but he who aspires to be a hero must drink brandy."
Samuel Johnson

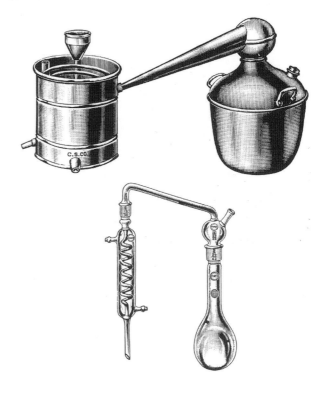

See "Hydrometer" and "Beer Tap."

"ευρηκα. ευρηκα."

"I've found it. I've found it." shouted Archimedes as he jumped from his bathtub. Not the soap, but the concept of specific gravity: the number of times a certain volume of matter is heavier or lighter than an equal volume of water. The specific gravity of a solid is found by immersing it in water and measuring the volume of water it displaces. A hydrometer measures the specific gravity of a liquid by the same means- only the solid is a hydrometer.

Hydrometer

A hydrometer measures the specific gravity of liquids and, by extension, the alcohol or sugar content of liquids, especially wine and liquor. Since taxes for liquor are based on proof or percentage alcoholic content, the hydrometer became a tool of the Revenuer in both England and the United States. Today, "proof" equals twice the percentage of alcoholic content. Originally, proof had a different meaning. Proof spirit was a mixture of alcohol and water with a specific gravity of 0.92. If a spirituous beverage was poured over gun powder and the gun powder could not be ignited, the beverage was considered under proof. If the gun powder could be ignited, the beverage was over proof.

If the proof of the pudding is in the eating, there must be a better test of proof for alcoholic beverages.

This brass hydrometer and weights are gold plated. There are ten weights and a mercury thermometer in a mahogany case.

About 1894.

Markings on celluloid plaque on top of case lid:

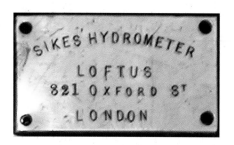

William Robert Loftus, 321 Oxford St. W., London, is listed as a hydrometer and saccharometer maker in 1894.

See "Alembic or Still" and "Beer Tap."

Hydrometers - same type, quality and period -
1978 $60
1998 $190
2003 $275
2004 $450

Analytical Balance

On the instigation of Marat and order of the National Assembly, France guillotined its greatest scientist in 1794. Antoine Lavoisier's profound discovery: *the total weight of all the products of a chemical reaction are exactly equal to the total weight of the reacting substances.* His proof of this principle finally distinguished chemistry from alchemy. His primary investigative tool was the analytical balance used in thousands of measurements.

Also termed a "precision balance," this balance has a mahogany case with glass on four sides. There are two drawers and access doors on both sides and front. There are three leveling screws. The scale itself is brass and polished steel. A front knob is used to rest the pans on supports. Pans are suspended from agate bearings on knife edges. The beam rests on an agate bearing and knife edge. The beam is indexed. Next to the column, there is a hanging pointed plumb bob over a ring. The plumb bob centers in the ring when the balance is level, an improvement of Fortin, a French instrument maker.

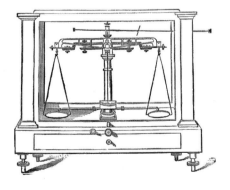

Last quarter of the 19th century

Length: 21 1/2 in.
Height: 20 1/4 in.
Width: 9 5/8 in.

Markings on base of column: *A. Ruprecht Wien*

See "Torsion Balance" and "Steelyard."

This balance would be sensible to about one tenth of a milligram. Generally, this form of analytical balance was the most accurate until the introduction of electronic balances capable of measuring to a millionth of a gram. The United States standard for weight is an iridium-platinum cylinder kept at the National Bureau of Standards. This weight is a copy of the international standard kept by the French government, an ironic and unacknowledged memorial to Lavoisier's masterful measurements.

Analytical balance - same type, quality and period - 2003 - $475

Barograph

Florin: "Why should I carry mercury to the top of the mountain? Mercury has wings. Let him fly there himself."

Blaise: "Mercury is the god of science. For the sake of science, I pray you do what I cannot. Take this barometer up the mountain and measure the air pressure at its peak."

In 1648, Blaise Pascal, a physically frail but brilliant French mathematician and physicist, persuaded his brother-in-law, Florin Périer, to carry a mercury barometer to the peak of Puy de Dome, a 5,000-foot mountain. The purpose: to find out if atmospheric pressure decreased with altitude. It did. The mercury barometer was an awkward instrument for measuring air pressure in the field. Eventually, the aneroid barometer was used for these measurements and calibrated as an altimeter.

Lucien Vidie invented the aneroid barometer in 1843. "Aneroid" means without fluid, a requisite of all previous barometers. The aneroid barometer has a metal bellows enclosing a vacuum (sylphon cell). A set of levers connected to an indicator multiplies the change in height of the bellows due to changes in atmospheric pressure. The aneroid barometer may include some mechanism for temperature compensation for more accurate readings.

Vidie vigorously defended his patent rights to the aneroid barometer. Eugène Bourdon, an engineer, invented a pressure gauge that infringed Vidie's patent. In 1858, Vidie won 25,000 francs in a French court in damages from Bourdon. Vidie. Vidi. Vici.

A barograph records changing atmospheric pressure. The data is used in predicting weather. This aneroid barograph has nickel-plated works and winding key. Clockwork drives a drum wrapped with paper. The case is mahogany and glass. The front lever adjusts the pressure of the pen against the drum.

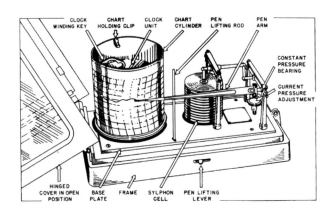

Early 20th century barograph.
Length: 12 in. Height: 6 1/2 in. Width: 5 1/2 in.

Markings on base plate: L (fouled anchor) M 325722

See "Wheel Barometer" and "Steam Pressure Gauge."

Barographs - same type, quality and period -
1978 - $225
1996 - $480
2005 - $930

Testing Sieves

0.75 in.

0.75 in.

0.50 in.

0.132 in.

0.0276 in.

0.0059 in.

Cement binds aggregate (sand, gravel or crushed stones) into the solid, rocklike mass of concrete. Concrete can fail with disastrous results. On May 1, 2003, a magnitude 6.4 earthquake strikes Bingöl, Turkey. Fatalities rise to 177 as buildings collapse. Many of the buildings could have survived the quake but for poor concrete. The concrete used in the collapsed buildings was low in quality and made with substandard aggregate. The concrete had strength values as low as one-third of those required by structural design. A quality standard for concrete is aggregate of consistent size for the specified concrete strength.

Technicians may use testing sieves to grade construction materials such as sand and gravel. These sieves are also used to grade industrial products such as pigments and abrasives, agricultural products such as grain and seeds, and anything that is commercially crushed or ground. Scientific researchers use these sieves; an example application is determining the sizes of plankton within a body of water. By using sieves, the technician measures the particle size distribution within a sample. Sieves are used singly or stacked so that material can be sifted through a progressively smaller mesh. After sifting, the contents of each sieve is weighed to find the quantity of different particle sizes composing the sample.

One may use mechanical sieve shakers, but the manual method is usually practical. Hold the individual sieve, provided with a snug fitting pan and cover in a slightly inclined position in one hand. Strike the side of the sieve sharply with an upward motion against the heel of the other hand at the rate of about 150 times per minute, while turning the sieve about one-sixth of a revolution at intervals of about 25 strokes. Seems a little more complicated than your grandmother's flour sifter.

Most sieves state the opening size in parts of an inch. Some also use millimeters, microns, a Tyler standard sieve numbering system or a National Bureau of Standards sieve numbering system. These brass sieves have an internal diameter of 8 in. and a height of 3 7/8 in. A complete set includes about 25 sieves, but usually only a few sieves within a limited range are used for testing a specific material. Sieve mesh sizes range from 0.00152 in. to 0.75 in. That's the hole story.

Testing sieves - same type, quality and period - 2005 - $60

Incremental Core Sampler

This tool is immediately recognizable by any dendrochronologist, but what's a dendrochronologist? Dendrochronologists date past events through tree ring analysis. They find the age of trees and they identify historic weather patterns and events, droughts, flooding, frosts, forest fires, volcanic and glacial activity. They also measure the recent history of chemical pollutants found in trees and timber. Given a sample, they could tell you the age and source of George Washington's wooden teeth or Captain Hook's peg leg (well, almost). Dendrochronologists use the incremental core sampler to extract a cylindrical sample from trees or timber. Tree rings occur as cross sections of the sample.

The hollow sampler shaft is screwed into the tree at a right angle to the tree trunk. A coating of beeswax on the shaft eases boring. When the sampler is pulled from the tree, a thin cylindrical core sample remains within the screw shaft.

At the left is the sampler disassembled and stored within the handle. On the far right is a semicircular and hollow rod used to remove the sample from the screw shaft.

Working length of the bore: 12 1/4 in.

Size: 5 1/2

Steel with brass end caps

Manufactured in Sweden by Pjos

Distributed by Keuffel & Esser Co.

Let's consider the life span of living things. On the short end, the May fly lives for only one day. Jeanne Louise Calment (1875-1997) holds the current longest record for human survival at 122 years. But, she did not outlive the giant tortoise (testudo elephantopus). A giant tortoise has lived for 177 years. The Pacific red sea urchin is thought to live for 200 years.

Biologists say that a limit to life makes room for better adapted versions of the same species. If this is true, then the longest-lived species has best adapted to its environment. That would be the sequoia. The longest tree-ring record is from a sequoia, spanning 8,700 years. Regrettably, the sequoia has not adapted to the chainsaw.

Incremental core sampler - same type, quality and period - 2006 $52

112

Microscope

Georges Oberhäuser, a Parisian microscope maker, popularized the drum microscope in France in 1835. This microscope with its large drum may appear awkward, but the drum inexpensively provides a sturdy support for the tube and stage. As lenses increased in magnification, sturdier support was needed to minimize vibration. A downside was the stiff necks and sore backs of the users due to the rigid pillar design.

This is a French Oberhäuser type microscope. It dates from about 1850 and is the largest of this type made by Nachet. Camille Sebastion Nachet (1799-1881) was formerly employed by Chevalier. He established his own firm about 1840. His earliest microscopes were of the drum type seen here. By 1890, his firm had adopted the inclinable pillar structure.

Height with prism for angled viewing: 13 in.

Diameter of stage: 3 3/4 in.

Markings on barrel support: Nachet Opticien à Paris
16 Rue Serpente

Manufactured before 1863.

The watered silk-lined, dovetailed, mahogany case for this microscope includes many accessories:

>   Three eyepieces (one cracked)
>   Ten objective lenses
>   Four condensers
>   Polarizing objective
>   Substage polarizer
>   Fish box
>   Compressor
>   Micrometer "Micrometre Millimetre en 100 Parties"
>   Prism insert for angled viewing

But, no Leiberkühn.

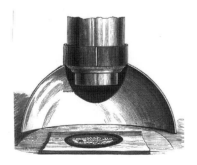

What's a *Leiberkühn*, anyway? You are a distinguished forensic pathologist with a difficult case. You place an opaque bone chip on a slide on the microscope stage. When you view it, all you really see is a silhouette, a darkened fragment with a light outline. You can't tell whether it's an animal or human bone fragment that was found in the incinerator. To illuminate an opaque object on the stage, one needs top-down lighting. This is provided by a concave reflector fitted to the objective, a Leiberkühn. As soon as it's in place, you can see from the texture of the surface that you have a bit of mother-of-pearl button. No bones about it. Case unsolved.

Microscopes - same type, quality and period -	
1980	$500
1999	$650
2008	$1,300

Spectroscope

The Goodyear blimp with its flashing sign floats because it's filled with 202,707 cubic feet of helium. This lighter-than-air and inert gas was first recognized as a new element by Pierre Janssen in 1868. With a spectroscope he identified the element in the sun's spectrum. At the time, no known element on Earth produced the same spectrum. In 1895, Sir William Ramsey found helium on Earth in a uranium mineral. Due to the spectroscope, helium (after Helios) was found in the Sun 27 year before it was discovered on Earth.

The Solar Spectrum

Substances when heated emit light with distinctive spectra. A spectroscope breaks light into its component spectrum to determine the nature of the light's source. Identifying a substance by means of its spectrum is complicated in that the same substance may emit different spectra at different temperatures. The spectroscope has been used to identify new elements, to develop atomic and molecular models, to explore the dimensions of the universe and to control manufacturing materials and processes.

A spectroscope in its simplest form, such as this one, includes a variable slit for collimating a beam of light, a prism to disperse the light, and a lens. This is a direct-viewing, small brass pocket spectroscope. It has an adjustable slit aperture objective and a telescoping focus.

Markings on tube: Heele - Berlin. Heele was manufacturing spectroscopes in 1890.

Length extended: 4 1/8 in.
Length closed: 3 1/8 in.
Maximum diameter: 1 in.

Late 19th century (?)

Characteristics of light spectra can be measured with extraordinary accuracy. Suppose political scientists had an analogous device to measure the political spectrum with equal accuracy. What undiscovered element would they find?

A spectroscope of 1880

Spectroscope - same type, quality and period -
1999 $250

114

Flash Point Tester

You have heard of "flash point" used as metaphor as in: "The assassination of Archduke Franz Ferdinand at Sarajevo was the flash point igniting the First World War." A flash point is the lowest temperature at which the vapors of a volatile combustible substance will ignite when exposed to air and flame. The true significance of "flash point" is evident in the following tragedy.

On July 17, 1996, TWA Flight 800, a Boeing 747, was at an altitude of 13,800 feet on route from New York to Paris, France. The fuel was Jet A with a laboratory flash point of 100° F. Because of the lower pressure at 13,800 feet, the flash point drops to 85° F., making ignition more likely. A center wing fuel tank exploded. According to a controversial finding by the National Transportation Safety Board, a spark or electrical fire was supposed to have ignited the fuel vapor in the tank at a temperature above the fuel's flash point. The airplane fell to earth with 230 souls on board. None survived. After investigating, the National Transportation Safety Board recommended that designs or operational changes be implemented to preclude the use of air transports with explosive fuel/air mixtures in their fuel tanks.

In the mid-19th century, petroleum oil increasingly fueled domestic lighting. Because of accidental fires, local governments and citizens shared concern for the safety and flammability of illuminating oil in these lamps. About the same time, scientists devised measures of flammability. One of these is flash point. Flash point testers are used in standard tests for many industries. These tests relate to safe use and handling of flammable liquids such as paints and fuels and are often legally mandated. This is a tag closed cup tester. "Tag" is short for its inventor, Giuseppe Tagliabue of New York. It is an instrument with modern variations, some electronically automated. This tester finds flash points of liquids below a temperature of 200° F.

In this tester, a cup with spring-loaded sliding lid contains the sample liquid. The cup is partly submerged in a water bath heated by an alcohol burner. When the side knob is turned, the lid opens and a small flame fueled by a gas line tilts into the cup. This is done at predetermined temperature increments read from the thermometers. One thermometer takes the temperature of the sample. The other takes the temperature of the water bath. At the flash point temperature, the flame ignites vapors above the sample liquid.

This name plate from the tester is a rebus of the word "tag" in that it has the shape of a sales tag.

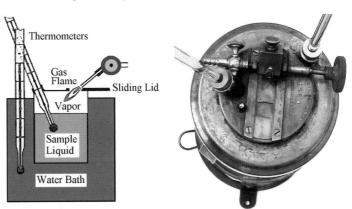

Brass ignition, lid mechanism and flash point cup. Copper burner, base and water bath.
Overall height: 9 in. Diameter at base: 4 1/4 in. Serial number: 4560
Patented August 7, 1917.

Flash point tester - same type, quality and period - 2006 $111

115

Crookes Tube

One holding two contradictory concepts in his mind at the same time is either a genius or a fool. William Crookes (1832-1919) qualifies as the former. He was a brilliant chemist, physicist and a spiritualist. He discovered the element thallium, invented the radiometer and investigated psychic phenomena. Crookes referred to the flow of electrons in a vacuum as "radiant matter."

Crookes said: "We have seen that in some of its properties Radiant Matter is as material as this table, whilst in other properties it almost assumes the character of Radiant Energy. We have actually touched the border land where Matter and Force seem to merge into one another, the shadowy realm between Known and Unknown which for me has already had peculiar temptations."

This is a tube designed by Crookes to demonstrate that electrons flow in straight lines in a vacuum and that the beam can be interrupted by metal. Electrons stream from the cathode (electron emitter) at the small end of the tube through the vacuum in the tube. Electrons passing the metallic Maltese Cross strike the front of the tube, causing it to fluoresce. Electron flow interrupted by the cross casts a non-fluorescent shadow of the Maltese cross on the front of the tube. The cross is hinged and may be folded over by tilting the tube to demonstrate electron flow without interruption. Unknown to Crookes, the electron beam striking the metal cross produced X-rays. Crookes may have used the shape of a Maltese cross because the Latin for "cross" is *crux,* sounding like his own name. This vacuum tube is a precursor of the cathode ray and television tubes.

Radiometer

A radiometer is a glass bulb containing a vacuum and a rotating spindle with four vanes. One side of each vane is black and the other is silvered or white. The vanes rotate when exposed to light. Crookes supposed the motive force was light itself. Subsequent researchers found that the relatively few remaining molecules of gas in the radiometer were heated by infrared radiation at the low end of the light spectrum and their resulting movement and collision with the vanes caused the vanes to rotate. To the technically unsophisticated, the movement of a radiometer with no evident force might seem supernatural.

A 19th-century Crookes tube

Length of tube: 9 in. Widest diameter: 2 1/2 in.

Crookes tube - same type, quality and period - 2006 - $190

116

Phrenological Bust

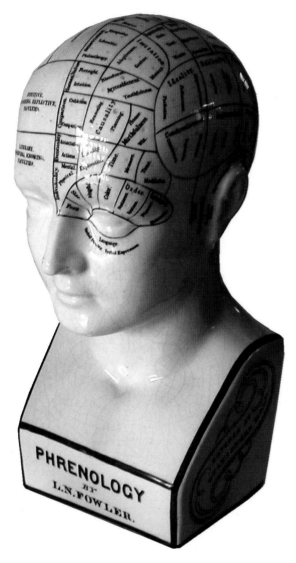

On the back of bust:

> For thirty years I have studied Crania and living heads from all parts of the world and have found in every instance that there is a perfect correspondence between the conformation of the healthy skull of an individual and his known characteristics. To make my observations available I have prepared a Bust of superior form and marked the divisions of the Organs in accordance with my researches and varied experience.

> L.N. Fowler

"Walt, *Leaves of Grass,* is a delightful collection of your poetry. I'd be happy to finance its publication." Words to that effect were spoken by Lorenzo Niles Fowler, a practitioner and promoter of phrenology and a good friend of Walt Whitman. He did, indeed, finance the first edition. Fowler moved from New York to London in 1860 and remained in England the rest of his life promoting the "science" of phrenology.

Walt Whitman

Both Lorenzo Niles Fowler and his phrenological bust are just a bit crazed. The bust is white ceramic with cobalt blue striping around the base. It dates from about 1860-1865. Height: 12 in.

The "science" of phrenology, reading character from the shape of the skull, was a 19th-century fad that proved baseless. It had the same relationship to psychology as astrology had to astronomy. Medical researchers continue to map the brain, but they focus on function, not character. Specific areas have been identified controlling speech, hearing, memory, taste, touch, abstract thought, balance, coordination and so on.

Phrenology, n. The science of picking the pocket through the scalp. It consists in locating and exploiting the organ that one is a dupe with.

The Devil's Dictionary, Ambrose Bierce

Fowler Phrenological busts - same type, quality and period -
1995 $ 900
1996 $ 900
1997 $ 925

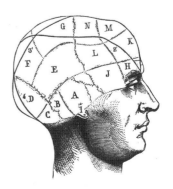

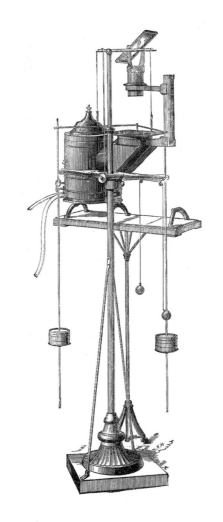

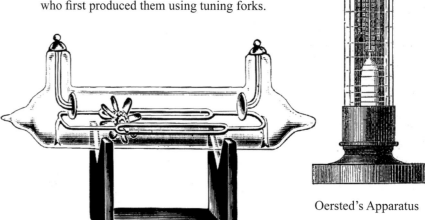

Binocular Microscope

J. L. Riddel of New Orleans developed the first practical binocular microscope in 1851. This is a Ross-Zentmyer model of 1878.

Fortin Barometer

The barometer takes many forms. This one, adapted for scientific uses, includes a screw and adjustable cistern for adjusting the height of the mercury for each observation. A thermometer is attached. See "Barograph" and "Wheel Barometer."

Harmonograph

This instrument traces the combined effects of the oscillations of two pendulums on a piece of smoked glass. It also projects these figures on to a screen. These are known as Lissajous figures after Jules Antoine Lissajous (1822-1880), a French mathematician who first produced them using tuning forks.

Crookes Railway Tube

The railway tube was inititially thought to show the force of an electron beam striking paddles on a wheel and rolling it along a glass track. Later research proved the electrons striking the paddles generated heat which moved the paddles in much the same way a radiometer's vanes are turned. See "Crookes Tube."

Oersted's Apparatus

This instrument demonstrates the transmission of pressure by fluids.

A few more examples of scientific technology

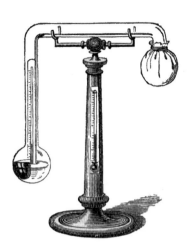

Hygrometer

Finds relative humidity by comparison of the temperature of the black bulb on the left with external temperature after the bulb on the right is moistened with ether and condensate forms on the black bulb.

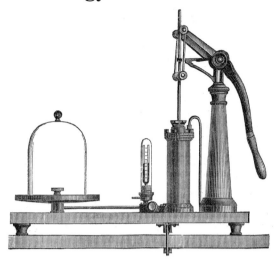

Vacuum Pump

Used in experiments relating to heat, chemistry and the behavior of gasses. A classic experiment is an alarm clock in the bell jar that cannot be heard because of the vacuum.

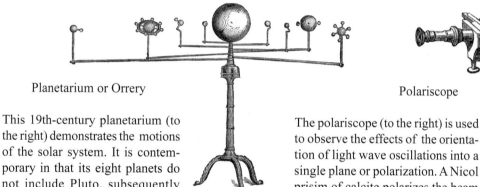

Planetarium or Orrery

This 19th-century planetarium (to the right) demonstrates the motions of the solar system. It is contemporary in that its eight planets do not include Pluto, subsequently discovered, but now demoted from planetary status. The orrery takes its name from the English 4th Earl of Orrery who was the patron of the instrument maker, John Rowley.

Polariscope

The polariscope (to the right) is used to observe the effects of the orientation of light wave oscillations into a single plane or polarization. A Nicol prisim of calcite polarizes the beam of light which is then reflected off of sample materials.

Coulomb's Electrometer

A torsion balance (to the right) used to measure weak electrical potential. The torsion balance employs a twisting wire and is extraordinarily sensitive. Coulomb used it to determine the law of electrical attraction.

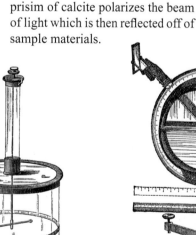

Refractometer

Includes a chamber for measuring the refraction (bending) of light through liquids. Both the angle of incidence and angle of refraction are measured.

Scientific technology update

The popular image of the Eureka discoveries of a brilliant scientist working alone in his own laboratory has little to do with modern research. In the late 20th century, scientific research became a team effort. This change was due partly to the greatly increased complexity of the research questions addressed and partly to the vastly increased cost of scientific research tools. Government and foundation funding required not only individual, but institutional accountability. Here are a few examples of these research tools and their price tags.

The Hubble Space Telescope orbits the Earth at a height of 300 miles. It is about the size of a school bus and powered by two 25-foot solar panels. Its primary mirror is 8 feet in diameter. Because of its location above the atmosphere, it provides images of unprecedented clarity. Starting in 1990, images from the Hubble dramatically increased our understanding of the surface features and composition of planets, the life cycle of stars, the nature of black holes, the size and composition of galaxies, and finally the age and expansion of the universe- all at a cost of 1.5 billion dollars.

Accelerators are used to investigate subatomic particles by colliding one with the other. The more powerful the collision, the smaller the particles. The smallest so far, quarks, come in six flavors with exotic names: charm, strange, truth, beauty, up, down. As the particles get smaller, the energy and dollars needed to produce them get larger. The largest accelerator is at CERN in Switzerland. It has a circumference of 17 miles and overlaps the border between Switzerland and France. At CERN, a hadron collider is under construction. Its estimated cost: 8 billion dollars and it is running over budget.

The world's fastest supercomputer, located at Lawrence Livermore, can perform 280.6 trillion floating point calculations per second. IBM named this computer Blue Gene/L. Its dedicated use is the simulation of nuclear explosions in place of actual nuclear testing. It cost the taxpayers 100 million dollars.

The flow cytometer, used in the biological sciences, sorts cells, measures cell surfaces and analyzes DNA. It can sort cells at a rate as high as 25,000 cells a second. For measurements, the cytometer exposes cells or cell materials to laser light and measures the wavelengths of the resulting fluorescent and reflected light. At $500,000 per instrument, the flow cytometer is a feasible investment for many biological laboratories.

The scanning tunneling microscope holds the record for the greatest optical enlargement of matter. The microscope uses an electron flow to a surface under observation to control the movement of a probe. The probe maps that surface. This microscope can resolve images as small as a tenth of the width of a hydrogen atom or one hundred-billionth of a meter. Images from the microscope helped to explain the performance of semiconductors. At a cost of $50,000, you'll find these microscopes in the bargain basement of scientific technology.

In theory, research results justify the huge cost of developing and operating modern research tools. But, there is a problem; institutional and governmental bureaucracy can stifle creative research. Is management science up to the task of managing science?

7 MEASURING THE LAND

Pocket surveying compass
Surveyor's compass
Alidade
Planimeter
Wye level
Dumpy level
Theodolite
Hand level
Abney level
Surveyor's chain
Surveying steel tape
Clinometer
Optical square
Mining dip needle
Station pointer

Surveyors should have earned the gratitude of generations of English school boys. In an old English custom called "beating the bounds," school boys marched around the parish boundaries once a year. They might be whipped or have cold water thrown on them as they passed important boundary landmarks. The intent was to fix the boundaries in the minds of the children. Thanks to surveyors, maps replaced memorized boundaries and the barbarism of beating the bounds.

George Washington was one of those surveyors, shown above at work and holding a surveyor's chain. He conducted his first survey at the age of 17. He held appointments as surveyor of Virginia and county surveyor, positions that enabled him to acquire valuable acreage. As a land speculator, he owned more than 65,000 acres of desirable real estate at one point in his career.

One of the surveying instruments Washington owned was a surveyor's compass made by Benjamin Rittenhouse of Philadelphia, colonial America's foremost scientific instrument maker. As colonists and pioneers moved west, occupying new territory, surveys were in demand and surveying instruments were valued. None of the instruments in this section are from the colonial period, but some are direct descendents.

In the 18th and early 19th centuries, land in America was cheap, often costing less than a dollar an acre. When large areas were surveyed, the additional effort needed by a surveyor for very accurate work was not worth the additional cost to the landowner. As time passed, landmarks were lost, forgotten or destroyed. Trees died, stones moved and streams and rivers changed their course. Inaccurate surveys and lost landmarks have contemporary consequences. Much of the work of modern surveyors is correcting ancient boundaries, thus increasing litigation for lawyers and the burden of courts through boundary disputes. Curiously, another President, Abraham Lincoln, was first a surveyor and then a lawyer.

Surveying Technology Time Line

Approximate Year of Manufacture of Objects in this Chapter		Year of Significant Events
	1574	Theodolite invented
	1606	Surveying chain invented
	1740	Surveyors level invented
Surveyor's chain	1850	
Optical square	1890	
Wye level	1891	
Surveying tape	1892	
Pocket surveying compass	1895	
Dumpy level	1895	
Theodolite	1895	
Clinometer	1895	
Alidade	1900	
Planimeter	1900	
Mining dip needle	1906	
Abney level	1906	
Station pointer	1920	
Hand level	1929	
Surveyor's compass	1940	
	1972	Satellite land use mapping

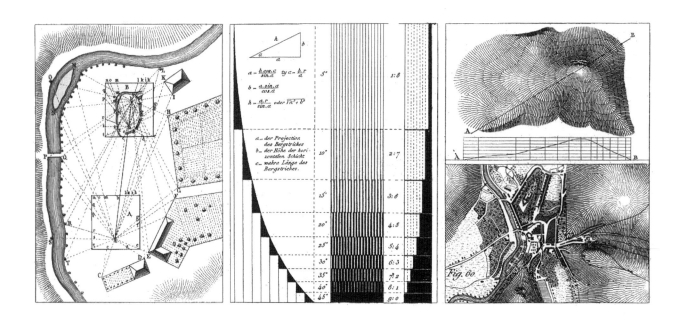

Pocket Surveying Compass

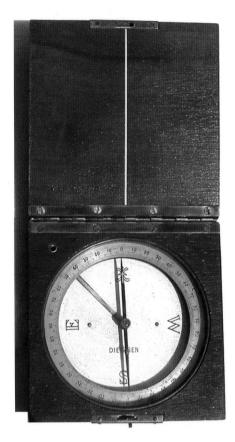

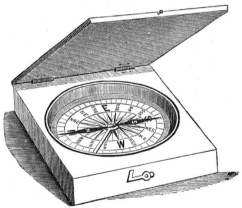

This is a surveying compass of a type made for more than two hundred years. It is a very tenuous link between Karl Marx and Lewis and Clark. A very similar mahogany-cased compass was carried by Lewis and Clark on their northwest discovery expedition of 1804, now in the collection of the Smithsonian Institute. Merriwether Lewis purchased the compass in Philadelphia for $5 and carried it on the 7,000-mile expedition.

Lewis and Clark recorded compass readings coordinated with their celestial navigation readings at many locations. Two hundred years later, Professor Robert Criss used this data to calculate the change in magnetic declination (the local horizontal angular distance between geographic north and magnetic north) for these readings. He found that, at a point near St. Louis, magnetic declination had changed almost eight degrees over the two centuries.

The case of this compass is mahogany with a bone strip used for sighting. When the lid is closed, a pin locks the compass needle. The compass circle is not divided into 360 degrees, but four quadrants of 90 degrees each. The reversal of East and West on the compass face shows that this is a surveying compass. It would have been used for preliminary or approximate surveys. The compass face is silver plated. The pointed top of the latch may be used as a sight.

Size: 3 5/8 in. square.   Thickness: 1 1/8 in.

Manufacturer: Dietzgen

Eugene Dietzgen (1862-1929) was born in Uckerath, Germany, and emigrated to the United States in 1878. He was employed by Keuffel & Esser in New York. He founded the Luhring & Dietzgen Company in Chicago in 1885. In 1891, it became Eugene Dietzgen & Co. The company distributed and manufactured surveying instruments, slide rules and drafting tools. The Dietzgen Corporation is still in business.

"Workers of the world, unite." This is the last sentence of *The Communist Manifesto* and an article of faith for Joseph Dietzgen, father of Eugene Dietzgen. Joseph Dietzgen was an internationally respected philosopher of social-democracy and an acquaintance of Karl Marx, who recommended Dietzgen's writings. Joseph Dietzgen defended the Haymarket anarchists in socialist publications during their trial and imprisonment. He died in Chicago in 1888. There is no account of his involvement in his son's capitalist enterprise.

See "Magnetic Navigational Compass" and "Surveyor's Compass."

Surveying compass - same type, quality and period - 1999 $100
2004 $210

Surveyor's Compass

A surprising number of American historical figures were surveyors at some time in their careers. Among these is John Brown. In a final letter to his family, he refers to religion as a compass in a boisterous ocean. His own surveyor's compass was a prized possession and in his last will and testament, completed on the night before his execution, he left it to his eldest son. On December 2, 1859, John Brown was hanged for his attempted insurrection at Harper's Ferry, Virginia.

John Brown

A surveyor's compass has sights and bubble levels and is used to find direction relative to magnetic north. It derived from the graphometer and circumferentor in the mid-18th century. For most of the 18th and 19th centuries, the surveyor's compass was the most common surveying instrument. It was used where the much greater accuracy (and expense) of a theodolite or transit was not required.

The most common 18th and early 19th-century surveyor's compasses had wood rather than brass cases. Compass cards were often printed engravings (some printed by Paul Revere) and were often the same cards as used in nautical compasses. "East" and "West" are reversed on later surveying compasses so that reading the north end of the needle shows the direction in which the instrument is sighted, the instrument bearing relative to magnetic north. This reversal of cardinal points may seem a little confusing. In contrast, John Brown's moral compass clearly indicated abolition in a war of North and South.

This surveyor's compass has foldable sighting vanes, two cross bubble levels, a vernier and a needle lock. The case is cast brass and 4 7/8 in. in diameter and the sighting vanes are 3 3/4 in. high. It was manufactured for military use by W. M. Welch Mfg. Co., Chicago.

The military has a long history in civil engineering and surveying, beginning with the Roman army's construction of roads, walls and aqueducts. The U.S. Army Corps of Engineers is a direct heir of this tradition.

A 19th-century surveyor's compass

W. M. Welch (1856-1940) founded the W. M. Welch Mfg. Co. in Chicago in 1906. Initially, the company developed and marketed educational scientific and laboratory equipment and later manufactured equipment and instruments for scientific research and engineering. In 1968, the company merged with the E. H. Sargent Company.

See "Pocket Surveyor's Compass."

Surveyors compass - same type, quality and period - 2006 - $123

Plane Table Alidade

An alidade is a movable sighting device or sighting rule used primarily in surveying or navigation. The term derives from an Arabic word for a revolving radius of a graduated circle. Examples are the sighting vanes on an astrolabe, the sighting vanes on a pelorus or dumb compass and the sighting vanes used to draw sightlines on a map or plot on a plane table in surveying. Tycho Brahe, the Swedish astronomer, had a quadrant with an alidade 19 feet in length. Alidades take many forms; modern alidades are equipped with telescopes instead of sighting vanes and may have vertical scales for determining angular elevation.

The concept of the alidade could be as old as the earliest human hunter sighting his prey along the shaft of an arrow. Possibly, the first verifiable attempt to scientifically understand the universe occurred in about 2400 BC. Stone-age men at Stonehenge used alidades. Stonehenge was an astronomical observatory. Wooden objects discovered in a nearby tumulus first thought to be fragments of a shield are now described as the remains of an alidade and plane table used in mapping stars from the observatory.

An alidade this small and portable would probably be used in the field for rough or preliminary mapping or possibly for military purposes. This simple brass alidade has an unusual form and is of German manufacture. It includes a compass with needle lock and a circular bubble or bulls eye level (now dry). One sighting vane is a notch and the other is a wedge, similar to gun sights. There are scales engraved on either edge. Two engraved scales, each of different unit length, with diagonal divisions are on the face. One edge scale and diagonal scale is labeled Met: 1:25000 (probably units per kilometer) and the other edge and diagonal scale is labeled DS: 1:25000 (probably units per *die Seemeile* or nautical mile of 1,853.2 meters).

About 1900 (?)

Other markings on lower left corner: B 41

On upper right corner: Gebr. Wichmann Berlin
Gebr. = *Gebrüder* or "brothers"

Length: 8 1/4 in. Width: 1 7/8 in.

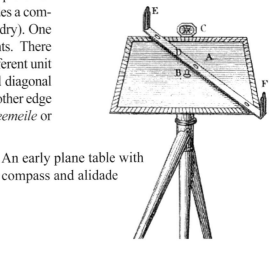

An early plane table with compass and alidade

Alidade - same type, quality and period -
1981 $40
1997 $150

125

Here is Amsler's dilemma. Professor Amsler has only two pieces of peanut brittle left for himself and a friend. He wants the largest piece, but both pieces are so wildly irregular, he can't tell which is larger. How can he find the areas of each piece? He could use his adjustable ratio planimeter.

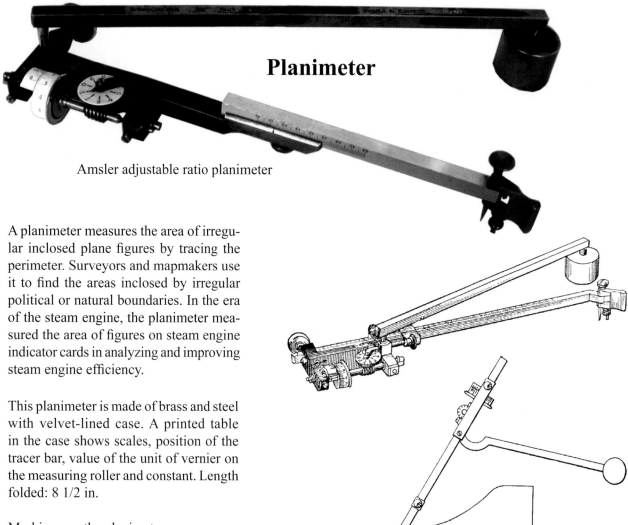

Planimeter

Amsler adjustable ratio planimeter

A planimeter measures the area of irregular inclosed plane figures by tracing the perimeter. Surveyors and mapmakers use it to find the areas inclosed by irregular political or natural boundaries. In the era of the steam engine, the planimeter measured the area of figures on steam engine indicator cards in analyzing and improving steam engine efficiency.

This planimeter is made of brass and steel with velvet-lined case. A printed table in the case shows scales, position of the tracer bar, value of the unit of vernier on the measuring roller and constant. Length folded: 8 1/2 in.

Markings on the planimeter:

G. Coradi/Zurich Switzerland Keuffel & Esser Co. New York
No 26138

Professor Jacob Amsler of Switzerland invented this form of planimeter in about 1856. Some of these are fixed ratio for a specific mapping scale. This planimeter, a later version, has a variable ratio feature. It dates from about 1900. As to finding the largest piece of peanut brittle, he could simply weigh the two pieces. We don't really know whether Professor Amsler liked peanut brittle or not.

See "Steam Engine Indicator."

Planimeters - same type, quality and period
1978 $95
1999 $200

126

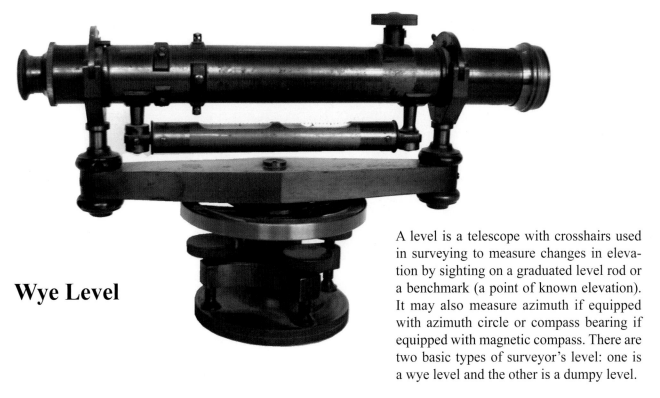

Wye Level

A level is a telescope with crosshairs used in surveying to measure changes in elevation by sighting on a graduated level rod or a benchmark (a point of known elevation). It may also measure azimuth if equipped with azimuth circle or compass bearing if equipped with magnetic compass. There are two basic types of surveyor's level: one is a wye level and the other is a dumpy level.

Why is a wye level called a "wye" level and a dumpy level called a "dumpy" level? The telescope of a wye level rests in Y-shaped brackets. The telescope can be removed and its direction reversed in these brackets. Jonathan Sissons of London invented the wye level in the 1720s. The telescope of the dumpy level is fixed to its base and cannot be removed from its mounting. "Dumpy" means short and stout. Gravatt's Improved Level with a fixed telescope, introduced in 1830 in England, was short with a wide aperture. To surveyor's of the time, this level appeared "dumpy" compared to other levels. The adjective stuck.

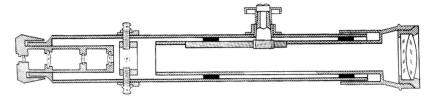

A laser beam blasted both wye and dumpy levels into obsolescence. Because of its accuracy and easy operation, only the laser level survives.

This brass wye level has a silvered vernier and azimuth circle. It has a single, long bubble level. The level includes four leveling screws and one rotational locking screw. The thumbwheel on top of the barrel focuses the telescope. The vernier reads 60-0-60. The telescope length: 10 3/4 in. Markings on the scope base:

>   Keuffel & Esser Co. New York 12694
>   Patented Dec. 3, 89. Aug. 12, 90. May 26, 91.

Wilhelm J. D. Keuffel and Herman Esser founded the firm of Keuffel & Esser in 1867. The firm incorporated in New Jersey in 1889, the year of the earliest patent on this level.

James W. Queen & Co. Catalog 1879

Wye levels - same type, quality and period -
1980 - $340
1999 - $400

127

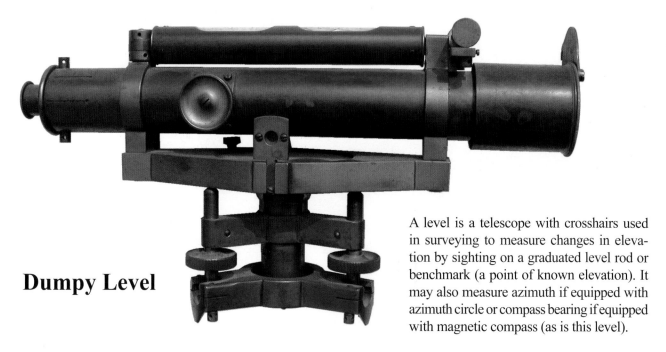

Dumpy Level

A level is a telescope with crosshairs used in surveying to measure changes in elevation by sighting on a graduated level rod or benchmark (a point of known elevation). It may also measure azimuth if equipped with azimuth circle or compass bearing if equipped with magnetic compass (as is this level).

"Dumpy" is lacking in graceful stature. When the dumpy level was first introduced in 1845, surveyors noted it was short and wide in comparison to its predecessor, the wye level. They described it as dumpy and the name stuck. But dumpy is not all bad. Because the telescope is permanently fixed in brackets, it proved more rugged than the wye level. Mae West agrees that dumpy is not all bad. She said, "A man can be short and dumpy and getting bald but if he has fire, women will like him."

This large, brass level has a compass and prismatic lens for reading the compass azimuth circle. The compass includes a thumbwheel compass needle lock. It has a large long bubble level and small cross bubble level above the telescope. The front lens cover swings aside. Graduations (30 to 0 to 30) are engraved on the extendible front lens sun shield with opposing narrow viewing slits in the shield.

Made by: W.F. Stanley in 1895

Overall length: 13 1/2 in. Overall height: 7 in. Diameter at front: 2 in.

Markings on base: Stanley's Patent

Markings on right side of barrel: Stanley, Great Turnstile Holborn London.

William Ford Stanley (1829-1909), was listed as a mathematical instrument maker at 4 & 5 Great Turnstile, WC London, in 1843. The firm was also listed as opticians and philosophical instrument makers at 13 Railway Approach, London Bridge SE, London, in 1894. Stanley not only manufactured surveying, nautical, optical and scientific instruments, he invented instruments, as well. He invented the *oograph*, "for an oologist for drawing eggs of birds in their natural sizes and proportions."

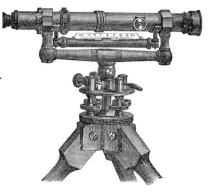

James W. Queen & Co. Catalog 1879

Take care in buying instruments attributed to W. F. Stanley; a California firm manufactures reproductions of instruments and marks them "Stanley, London." These instruments may have a persuasive antique patina.

See "Wye Level" and "Box Sextant."

Theodolite

Theodolite – a surveying instrument that measures both azimuth (horizontal angles) and angular altitude (vertical angles) to very great accuracy. Magnetic bearings are found with the theodolite's compass.

Surveying has its heroes. The foremost of these is Sir George Everest, in whose honor the mountain is named. He supervised the great trigonometric survey of India between 1823 and 1843. He overcame daunting obstacles: extremes of climate, disease, hostile tribes and almost impassable terrain. The India survey was an extraordinary achievement. The most accurate reference measurements were made with very large theodolites. These had azimuth circles of 36 inches diameter and altitude circles of 24 inches diameter. They were made especially for the survey.

George Everest

The theodolite shown is dwarfed by those used in India.

Diameter of azimuth circle: 6 1/4 in.
Diameter of altitude circle: 6 in.
Height to top of altitude circle: 13 1/2 in.
Length of scope fully extended: 12 1/2 in.

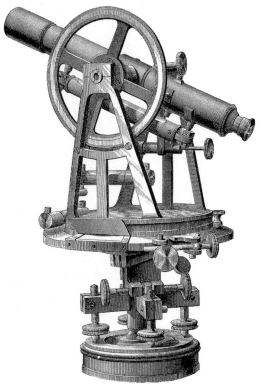

This brass theodolite includes a compass. The graduated azimuth and altitude circles are silver. The altitude circle has two verniers with two magnifiers. The azimuth circle has two verniers and one magnifier. Verniers are silver and read 20 to 0. Two small cross levels are located by the azimuth circle and a large level is fixed to the top of the scope. Both circles have fine tangent screw adjustment thumbwheels. For the instrument above the base plate, there is a fine tangent screw rotation adjustment with locking key and four leveling thumbwheels. Made in the fourth quarter of the19th century.

Markings on the altitude vernier: Lilley & Son London

John Lilley & Son, 10 London St. EC London, is listed as a mathematical instrument maker in 1894.

The earliest theodolite is dated 1574 and was made by Humphrey Cole, the most prominent Elizabethan instrument maker.

Theodolites - same type, quality and period - 1999 - $1,200

Hand Level

John Locke (1792 - 1856) was a physician, chemist, botanist, geologist, horologist, surveyor and inventor, just about anything you'd care to put on your resumé. He was an American Renaissance man in the tradition of Benjamin Franklin. Like Franklin, Locke was the stuff of legends. A man in Locke's home town had a watch that would not keep time. John Locke, the boy, had never owned or worked with watches. Yet, in a surprising gesture of trust, the man turned the watch over to the boy who repaired it with his penknife. Moral: the rewards of credulity are strictly legendary.

John Locke invented the hand level and described it as a "collimating level." He received a patent for it, No. 7477, on July 2, 1850. This example is based on Locke's design, shown below.

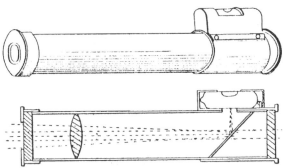

The hand level is used to find approximate differences in elevation in surveying: whether an object is at, above, or below the viewer's eye level. It may be used with a leveling rod for measurements relative to bench marks or established elevations. Since it contains no magnifying lens, it is used only for short distances, often at construction sites. On the right side of the sight, one sees the landscape and on the left side, an index line and level bubble. If the bubble is on the index line, the object next to the line is at one's eye level. If Fay Wray used a hand level, she would see King Kong's ankle.

All brass with leather holster and belt loop.

Length fully extended: 5 1/2 in. Tube diameter: 13/16 in.

Although marked "Keuffel & Esser Co. N.Y.", this hand level was almost certainly manufactured by Kuker-Ranken Inc. Seattle, and then distributed by Keuffel & Esser. The patent for this hand level, No. 1741422, was issued to O. J. Kuker on Dec. 21, 1929.

Hand level - same type, quality and period - 2004 - $50

Abney Level

For the scientific community, an experiment lacks validity unless it can be performed independently with the same results. This concept was the focus of a publication of science satire entitled *The Journal of Irreproducible Results.* William de Wiveleslie Abney (1843-1920) could have been the subject of an article. He invented infrared photography in the 1870's. Abney photographed a boiling tea kettle in the dark using an infrared sensitive emulsion of his own invention. His experiment was not successfully repeated until 1903. His more reliable invention was the Abney level.

Abney was a chemist and astronomer. He invented the Abney level while working for the School of Military Engineering in Chatham, England. The Abney level is basically a Locke hand level with an additional provision for measuring the angular distance of the object sighted above or below eye level. The image is vertically split between the object sighted and a rotatable bubble level. A horizontal index line divides the view. Degrees of the object sighted above or below eye level are read after the bubble is located on the index line. Since the bottom of the level is flat, it can be held against any plane surface to measure inclination. Surveyors use it for preliminary surveys. If the distance to the base of a vertical object is known, the Abney level can be used to find the object's height.

This brass Abney level is 6 in. long. Its scale is graduated from 90 to 0 to 90 degrees with a vernier and locking wheel. This design is unusual in that it includes a compass (note the surveyor's reversal of East and West). It was manufactured by Keuffel & Esser in about 1906. See "Locke Hand Level."

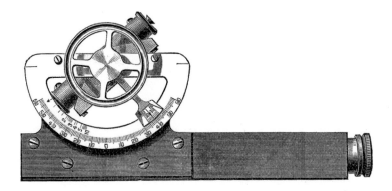

Abney level - same type, quality and period - 2008 - $142

Surveyor's Chain

In 1831, a length of grapevine served the purpose of a surveyor's chain in laying out Middletown, Indiana. When acreage cost pennies, the surveyor's accuracy was not as prized.

Before measuring tapes and electronics, surveyors used chains to measure distance. In English-speaking countries, these chains derive from Gunter's chain. Edmund Gunter (1581-1626), an English mathematician and inventor, invented the chain as a surveying measure consisting of 100 links, 66 feet in length. Most surveyor's chains include tally tags spaced along the chain. These tags have notches in them, one notch for every ten feet. A single Gunter's chain equals 66 feet, four rods or four poles. Eighty chains equal one mile and ten chains square equal one acre. A short, 33-foot Gunter's chain was also used.

How long is a piece of string? The same could be asked of a surveyor's chain. Although nominally 66 feet, links could be bent and connecting surfaces worn as the chain was dragged across rocks and through the undergrowth. Measuring up or down a slope with the chain introduced horizontal error, the greater or longer the slope, the greater the error. Where a tree or other obstacle blocked the measuring line, the chain might be laid around the obstacle or an estimate was made. Where a chain stretched over a stream or depression and sagged, additional error was introduced. To compensate, early surveyors tended to err on the side of additional length. Such an error was forgiveable and unlikely to trouble the landowner paying for the survey.

Presently, Electronic Distance Meters have replaced steel measuring tapes for distance measurement. They use either infrared signals or microwaves to measure distances up to 20 miles within an accuracy of three millimeters; quite an improvement over 8 inches in three chains, an early standard of accuracy.

This surveyor's chain, a two-pole chain, is of 10-gauge iron wire and 33 feet long. Circular rings connect the 50 chain links and triangular handles at each end of the chain. The chain includes an anti-twist joint in the middle. This is a short chain, half of a 66-foot Gunter's chain. This length is common in New England where plot sizes were small. Dated to the mid-19th century.

Since the errors of surveyors are merely venial while the sins of Jacob Marley are mortal, his chains are longer than Gunter's.

Surveyor's chain - same type, quality and period - 2008 - $157

Surveying Tape

The honor of inventing the steel surveying tape has many claimants.

1853: James. Chesterman of Sheffield, England, received a patent for a spring steel measuring tape.

1860: William H. Paine of Sheboygan, Wisconsin, received a patent for a tin-plated steel tape.

1867: Eddy & Co. of Brooklyn, New York, received a patent for a steel tape.

1868: Alvin J. Fellows of New Haven, Connecticut, secured a patent for a spring steel measuring tape.

1871: After studying the latitude and longitude of a lady's hooped skirt, Daniel M. Wheeler of Rutland, Massachusetts, designed a surveying tape using the steel tape from its framework.

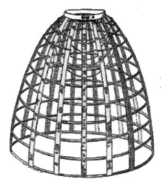

Hoop skirt frame

Justus Roe began manufacturing steel tape measures in 1865 in Patchogue, New York. This surveying tape is his work. At the time, engraving on steel was extremely expensive. To lower his costs, Roe marked intervals on his steel tapes with rivets and metal tabs.

Steel surveying tapes expanded and contracted according to temperature variations, causing errors in measurements. This remained a problem until the invention of invar, an alloy of nickel and steel with a very low coefficient of expansion in about 1900. Thereafter, invar tapes supplanted steel surveying tapes.

Distance on the tape is marked with a brass rivet every two feet, a brass tab every 5 feet and a copper tab every 10 feet.

Steel surveying tape: Brass frame, wood handle, overall height: 10 in. Maufactured by by Justus Roe & Sons, patented May 24 1892.

Surveying tape - same type, quality and period - 2008 - $55

Clinometer

"Angle of repose" is the maximum angle at which loose material will rest without sliding. That angle depends on the material's density, particle size and coefficient of friction. For snow, the angle of repose is variable, but generally about 75°. Bear in mind that 90° is straight down. So, 75° is too steep to ski.

Consider the skier looking at a 45° slope. That amounts to one foot down the slope for every one foot horizontally, a pretty steep grade. Only the most proficient skiers are inclined to tackle an incline of 60°.

Many ski resorts mark ski routes or trails with the slope indicated in degrees. They measure the slope angle with clinometers. A novice skier choosing to ignore the slope angle could very well find his own angle of repose at 0°.

In surveying, clinometers typically use a bubble or weight to locate angle of slope relative to the horizontal. They may do so by sighting devices or by contact as with this clinometer.

A clinometer is similar to a level but is used when angles other than 0° or 90° must be accurately determined. A side of this clinometer is placed on the surface and the arm with a bubble level is moved until horizontal; then the degree of inclination is read from the scale. This form of clinometer is uncommon and dates from the late 19th century. A clinometer of related design was used to find cannon elevation and was termed a "gunner's quadrant."

This clinometer is bronze and brass with scales from 0° to 90° with vernier. It has a bubble level, clamping screw and calibration adjustment. Its radius is 7 in. It was manufactured by W. & L. E. Gurley of Troy, N.Y.

Jonas Phelps and William Gurley founded this surveying instrument company in 1845. When Lewis E. Gurley joined the company in 1852, it became the W. & L. E. Gurley Company. The company was a very prominent manufacturer of surveying instruments.

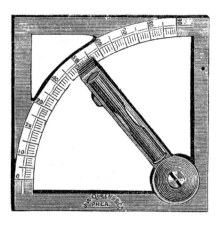

A 19th-century clinometer

Clinometer - same type, quality and period - 2006 - $123

Optical Square

Pythagoras (580 BC) was the first to call himself a philosopher, a lover of knowledge. He founded a school of followers who advocated temperate living and social harmony. Among the many maxims attributed to him are these:

> Put on thy right shoe first, and wash thy left foot first.

> Spit upon the clippings of thy nails and on the trimmings of thy hair.

> Keep far from thyself the vinegar cruet.

> Make thy libations to the deities by the ear.

The ultimate wisdom of these maxims is obscure, but the wisdom of his mathematical maxim was evident and earned him eternal fame.

> For a right triangle, the sum of the squares of the sides equals the square of the hypotenuse.

According to legend, in celebration of its discovery he sacrificed oxen to the deities.

For surveyors, the eternal triangle is Pythagorean. Two sides and a ninety degree angle give you the length of the hypotenuse. Sighting a marker at right angles to a line begins the process. A surveyor's cross staff, a device with viewing slits at right angles, was originally used to locate the approximate position of the surveyor's transit for more precise measurements. It was replaced by the optical square. A small hole in the case lets you look straight ahead over a half-height mirror while both mirrors reflect the images on your right just beneath the hole. This arrangement of mirrors is somewhat similar to that of a sextant.

King George III of England was fascinated by scientific instruments. He was the patron of George Adams, Sr. (1704-1772), one of the greatest instrument makers of his time. Adams invented the optical square in about 1740. He may very well have celebrated his invention with libations, but not by the ear.

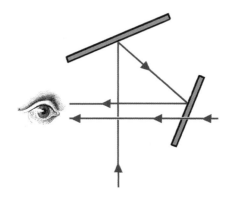

Stamped into the top: Pablo Ferrando
                              262 Sarandi
                              Montevideo

Brass case. Diameter: 2 1/8 in. Height: 1 1/8 in. With adjustment key.

Probably of late 19th-century English manufacture.

Optical square - same type, quality and period - 2006 - $120

Mining Dip Needle

Leprechauns beware! Guard your gold. Using a metal detector, a 38-year old Irish building contractor discovered a gold and amber horde in the county Tipperary. The treasure, from the 9th century A.D., was conservatively valued at $8 million.

In September of 1998, Colin Roberts of Wales discovered a cache of 3,750 Roman coins with his metal detector. The coins were buried at Monmouthshire about 296 A.D.

In November of 2004, Glyn and Glenys Jones used their metal detector to find gold bracelets and armlets in Berkshire, England. The treasure was buried in about 1300 B.C. Its value: about $180,000.

With a metal detector, Chris Bradshaw uncovered a Bronze-Age gold cup in Kent, England in 2001. Its value was about $500,000.

These are a few of thousands of hobbyists using metal detectors to uncover underground valuables. These detectors emit very low frequency radio waves to identify underground anomalies. They are infinitely more effective than the mining dip needle used until the mid-20th century.

The dip needle was putatively helpful in locating many metals and minerals. Practically, it located iron. In the hands of miners, it located deposits of iron ore. In the hands of plumbers, the dip needle located underground iron pipes. When the dip needle is held so that a dial edge faces magnetic north, the red (north) end of the needle tends towards zero. As the dip needle is moved over iron, the needle dips towards 90 on either side, indicating the proximity, density or quantity of iron.

This dip needle is brass, 3 3/8 in. in diameter and 1 in. thick. The graduations read 0 right and left to 90 at the center. The same scale is on front and back. A steel pin is inserted to attract the needle and lock it when not in use. The W. S. Darley Co. manufactured this dip needle. Founded in 1908, W. S. Darley Co. currently manufactures pumps and fire fighting equipment. See "Correcting Dip Needle."

From an 1894 Sears, Roebuck & Co. catalog:

No. 69840. Miners' Dip Needle Compass, used for prospecting for minerals. A well made and accurate dipping needle compass with brass rim and nickel plated dial. The needle points downward when mineral is located; instrument packed in neat morocco case. Each....$9.75

Mining dip needle - same type, quality and period - 2008 - $140

Station Pointer

Four ships crashed against the rocks of the Scilly Islands on the night of October 22, 1707. Almost 2,000 men lost their lives. The ships were from the fleet of British Admiral, Sir Cloudesley Shovell, returning from a victorious attack against the French navy. His navigators incorrectly advised him that their fleet was to the East of the Scilly Islands and well within the English Channel. This navigational error in longitude was fatal for Sir Shovell. His body was temporarily buried on the beach of St. Mary's Island in the Scillys. As a result of this tragedy, the British government founded the Board of Longitude and charged it with finding reliable means of determining one's longitude at sea. Almost 100 years later, British Captain Joseph Huddart visited Shovell's former burial site and, as a gesture of respect, measured its exact longitude.

Captain Joseph Huddart (1714-1816) had a distinguished career as a cartographer and hydrographic surveyor. Among his achievements: surveying the West coast of Sumatra, inventing machinery for the manufacture of rope, and inventing the station pointer or three-arm protractor.

A station pointer locates an unknown position in relation to three known positions. Though sometimes used in navigation, its primary use is in hydrographic surveying. Using two horizontal angles measured between three known and charted points, one adjusts the arms so that the beveled edges touch the three charted points. The center of the graduated dial becomes the charted point from which the angular measurements to the known points were made.

This U.S. Navy station pointer, No. 111, made by Keuffel & Esser has an overall length of 35 in., including arm extensions. It is brass and nickel-silver, an alloy of nickel, copper and zinc. The graduated circular dial with two verniers and clamps has a diameter of 6 1/2 in. Cylindrical fittings for the center of the dial include a pin for marking the chart, a centered hole for marking the chart, and cross hairs. This instrument dates from the early 20th Century. It, too, has been displaced by the Global Positioning System.

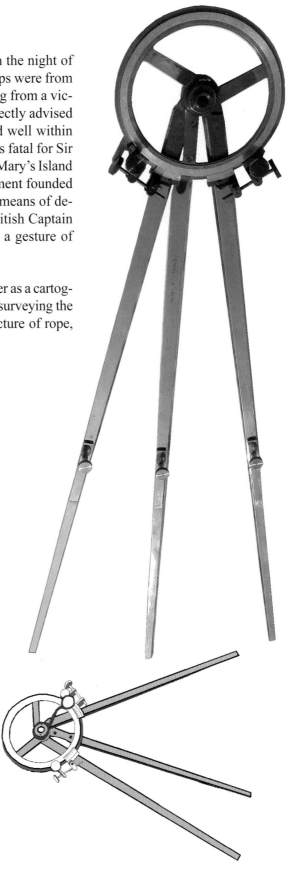

Station pointer - same type, quality and period - 2008 - $150

Plane Table

This is a plane table with a telescopic alidade. The surveyor plots the location of the plane table on a sheet. Then he plots the angles and distances to other objects on the sheet to scale through alidade sightings and distance measurements.

Level

Solar Transit

A transit permits the complete rotation of the telescope around its axis. Solar transits have special sights to track the sun to its meridian or highest point to identify true North.

Here, the addition of peep sights and a tripod converts a carpenter's spirit level into a surveyor's level.

Odometer or Hodometer

A carriage wheel drove this counter (to the left) of about 1890 to measure mileage. It would have been used more for mapping than for surveying.

Lamp Target

In mine surveying, the surveyor's target (to the right) had to be illuminated. This target included an oil lamp to back-light the target.

A few more examples of surveying technology

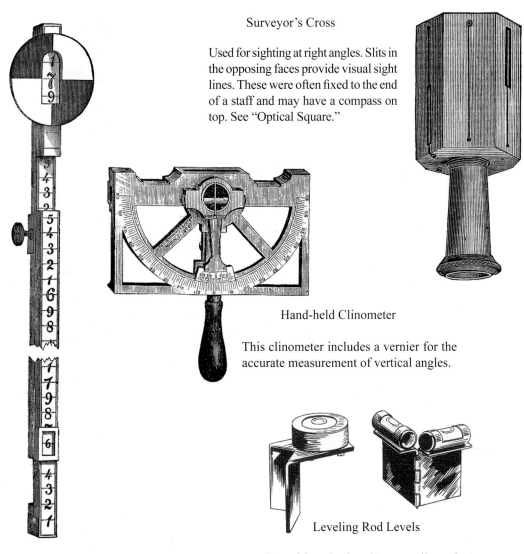

Surveyor's Cross

Used for sighting at right angles. Slits in the opposing faces provide visual sight lines. These were often fixed to the end of a staff and may have a compass on top. See "Optical Square."

Hand-held Clinometer

This clinometer includes a vernier for the accurate measurement of vertical angles.

Leveling Rod Levels

One of these is placed temporarily on the top of the leveling rod while it is being sighted to assure the rod is vertical.

Philadelphia Leveling Rod

A graduated rod adjustable in length to about 13 feet with a visual target and sighted through a surveyor's level to find differences in elevation. By vernier adjustment, the rod can be read to a thousandth of a foot.

Telescopic Alidade

This alidade, used for plane table surveying, has both a telescope and a graduated circle for reading vertical angles. See "Plane Table Alidade."

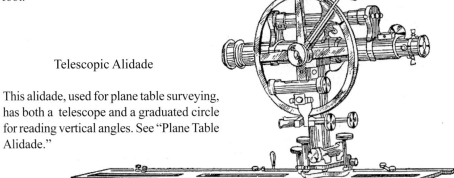

Surveying technology update

The march of civilization consists of the explorer followed by the soldier followed by the missionary followed by the trader followed by the surveyor. Historically, the surveyor had to contend with wild animals, hostile natives, rough country and bloodthirsty insects. He had to transport and set up fragile equipment. It was time-consuming and heavy work. Now, the heavy lifting is over. The optical level and theodolite, the compass and surveyor's tape are obsolete. We'll look at the instruments that replaced them.

The optical theodolite measures angular elevation and horizontal angles or azimuth. The angles are read from calibrated circles through magnifying lenses by the surveyor and recorded by him. In modern theodolites, these measurements are read and recorded electronically after the theodolite is optically sighted on the target. If we add the function of electronic distance measurement to this modern theodolite, it becomes a "total station."

Generally, electronic distance measurement (EDM) bounces electromagnetic radiation off of a reflector and measures radiation travel time to find distance to the reflector. Accurate sighting may be assured by automatic electronic adjustment for the reflected signal with maximum strength. Microwave EDMs measure distances up to 120 miles, laser light EDMs measure distances up to 4 miles and infrared EDMs measure distances up to 2.5 miles. All of these measurements are executed with very great accuracy and electronically recorded by a total station.

The most sophisticated total stations include a global positioning system (GPS) receiver. The receiver assigns electronically-recorded geographic coordinates to the survey stations. Finally, all of these electronic data gathered by the total station can be used by computer assisted design (CAD) software to produce a map of survey stations and traverse lines. This map may be superimposed over an aerial or satellite survey map. Using the total station has these advantages over conventional optical survey methods: easier to use, much speedier, much less labor intensive, less costly, and much more accurate.

For aerial surveys, aerial laser scanning is the ultimate tool. In a single airplane pass, a laser sweeps the terrain measuring the range and angle to the ground surface. This data is coordinated with continuous on-board GPS readings, inertial navigation input and digital camera images. The combined information produces a survey map, including elevations, with a scale as small as 1 to 1,000.

During World War II, General George Patton took his tanks across a river well ahead of the planned spearhead and then reported his position to Allied Headquarters. Field Marshal Montegomery told Patton he could not possibly be in the position he claimed because, according to the map, there was no bridge at that point. Patton said there *is* a bridge and that, "The map is not the territory." This statement is an eternal verity. Yet, it is an unlikely observation had the map been produced by laser scanning.

8 THE TOOL-USING ANIMAL

Bitstock
Mortise scribing gauge
Plow plane
Folding rule
Micrometer calipers
Universal bevel protractor
Machinists' level
Paint spray gun
Violinmakers molds
Plumb bob
Patternmakers tools
Blowtorch
Tufting tool

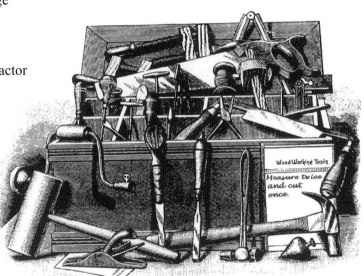

Thomas Carlyle said: "Man is a tool-using animal. Nowhere do you find him without tools; without tools he is nothing. With tools he is all." Our unique opposable thumb enables us to handle tools easily. Our ability to accurately throw sticks and stones proved hugely advantageous in competing with the intellectually superior, but dexterity-challenged great apes. By reducing competition, we bought time in which to develop the flint knife and stone hammer. Our craftsmanship improved with our tools and our tools improved with our craftsmanship. This cycle begat our ultimate tools.

Our ultimate tools are the robot and computer. In science fiction, they assume starring roles. What do these movies have in common? *2001: A Space Odyssey, Moonraker, Blade Runner, Terminator*. In each of them a computer or robot, tries to destroy its creator. This recurrent theme raises all kinds of psychological, moral, social and theological issues. Lucky for you, we're not going to explore them. But you might want to chew on this: Henry David Thoreau said, "Man has become the tool of his tools."

Tool Technology Time Line

Approximate Year of Manufacture of Objects in this Chapter		Year of Significant Events
	1550	Screwdriver invented
	1600	Exchangeable drill bits invented
	1638	Micrometer invented
	1797	Lathe lead screw invented
	1828	Combine invented
	1837	John Deere plow introduced
	1840	McCormick reaper introduced
Violinmakers molds	1850	
Bitstock	1860	Screw thread standardized
Plow plane	1860	Circular saw in general usage
	1861	Pneumatic drill invented
	1867	Milling machine invented
Mortise scribing gauge	1870	
	1880	Blowtorch invented
Machinists' level	1886	
Tufting tool	1888	
Patternmakers sculpting tools	1890	
	1895	Electric hand drill invented
Folding rule	1900	
Paint spray gun	1910	
Plumb bob	1910	
Blowtorch	1920	
Micrometer calipers	1935	

Bitstock

Our subject is boring, not inflicting ennui, but drilling holes. Chunks of wood with charred holes are found among the animal bones in ancient middens. These show that some keeper of the fire used the bow to rotate a stick in starting fires. A proto-carpenter noted these holes, fixed a hard point to the stick and invented the first bow drill. Its use is shown in Egyptian tomb paintings of 2,700 BC. Another form of drill is the bitstock.

"Crank" describes an eccentric notion or an eccentric motion. Originally, "cranky" meant crooked or bent out of shape. So, this bitstock is cranky, offset or shaped like a crank. A crank is used to convert reciprocal motion to rotary motion as in the crankshaft of an automobile and that is exactly the function of this bitstock's shape.

The bitstock or brace, permitting continuous rotary motion, originated in China and was first introduced to Europe in the 15th century. These bitstocks had the drill bit permanently fixed to the bitstock, so that a different bitstock was needed for each drill bit size. Why carry ten bitstocks when you could carry only one bitstock and ten drill bits? It took 200 years to solve this problem. In the 17th century, bitstocks with exchangeable drill bits were invented. Early drill bits were not twisted or spiraled, but hollowed half-cylinder segments similar to a gouging chisel. They were called "spoon bits." The bit in this bitstock is a combination twist drill and spoon or "pod," often used to start a hole for a spoon bit.

A bitstock is a bitstock is a bitstock. Not true because so many of them had special-purpose designs. Here are a few profession-specific bitstocks: blacksmith's bitstock, brewer's bitstock, carriage maker's bitstock, chair maker's bitstock, piano maker's bitstock, surgeon's bitstock, undertaker's bitstock.

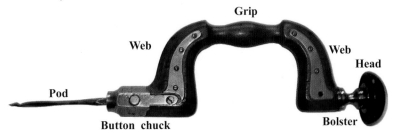

The bitstock shown here was probably made in England in the early 19th century. It has a brass button chuck, reinforcing plates and bolster. The head is ebony. The webs on this bitstock are curving, tapering octagons that flow gracefully into a comfortable grip. The shape is an elegant combination of curves and planes. It has been replaced by the electric power drill, much more effective, but not nearly as beautiful.

Stamped into the web: S. H. PEIRSON   GREGG 27 SLOAN SQ

Length from chuck to head: 14 in.

See "Electric Drill."

Bitstock - same type, quality and period - 2004 - $200

Mortise Scribing Gauge

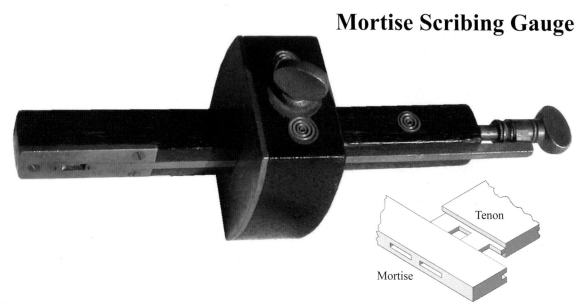

Tenon

Mortise

Some things are naturally joined together: Adam and Eve, tea and crumpets, rock and roll, spit and polish, politics and perjury, gin and tonic, nuts and bolts, mortise and tenon. At its best, joinery marries pieces of wood in a way that precludes divorce. There is no wiggle room in a mortise and tenon relationship.

Mortise: a hole cut in timber to receive a mating object or tenon. Tenon: a projection from a timber intended to fit a mating mortise. Mortise and tenon are used in framing and cabinetmaking to create a strong, interlocking joint. Pegs or wedges may be used to lock the mortise and tenon together. Such a joint works only if it is a neat, tight fit. The mortise gauge makes that fit possible. A mortise gauge has at least two points or spurs to scribe lines where a mortise is to be cut. The thumb screw at the rear of the gauge adjusts the thickness of the mortise, the distance between the spurs. The top thumb screw locks the fence of the gauge in place as an edge guide. The carpenter or cabinetmaker slides the fence along the edge of a board when scribing the lines.

Mortise and tenon joints are common in furniture and were once common in construction before metal hardware became cheap and generally available. One can still see these joints in the framing of old barns and churches. Such joints have lasted hundreds of years. Not surprising, considering that mortise and tenon joints were used in surviving Egyptian furniture made more than three thousand years ago.

Originally, a rectangular mortise hole began with two drill holes at either end of the mortise. Chisels squared up the hole and removed wood from between the holes. A right-angled corner chisel was sometimes used for these cuts. Now, power-mortising tools cut rectangular holes with a combination press-driven chisel and drill bit.

"Stay between the lines" is a good idea when driving a car or painting by numbers. The phrase has been elevated to a moral precept meaning "do the right thing." For the carpenter, the mortise scribing gauge provides the lines.

This gauge is rosewood with brass fence face and fittings.

Stamped on the fence, owner's name: V M MORGAN

Stamped on the fence, manufacturer: W. JOHNSON NEWARK N.J.

Overall length closed: 8 1/2 in.

Mortise gauge - same type, quality and period - 2004 - $60

Plow Plane with Adjustable Fence

"I say, Sir Roger, that maladroit mechanic jolly well bungled your wainscoting, what?" The English aristocracy would never have its paneled drawing rooms without the plow plane. The panels fit into channels. Try cutting a long, straight channel with a chisel and you turn good lumber into firewood. A plow plane neatly cuts these furrows or channels by using an adjustable fence, an edge-guide, to assure straight, even cuts.

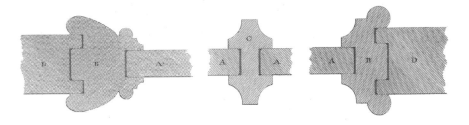

Plow planes were often beautifully crafted. They were so highly valued that some were made of rosewood or ebony, sometimes with ivory fittings. This is a mid-19th century example. The body is beech. The wood screws and wood nuts are apple, used because of its smooth density. Metal parts are brass and steel. It is marked "C.C. STILES," probably a craftsman and the proud owner. The Ohio Tool Company made this plow plane, model number 101. Founded in Columbus, Ohio in 1851, the Ohio Tool Company flourished until 1920. Its primary product was planes of various types.

Length: 12in.   Width:10 in.

Well-made tools of time-tested design have an intrinsic fitness of purpose. They speak directly of skill, craftsmanship and thoughtful care for the work to be done. Years of use are the ultimate caress of the artisan's hand. The term "quality" has been cheapened by advertising, but it is *true quality* that these tools exhibit and produce.

Plow plane - same type, quality and period
1994 $200

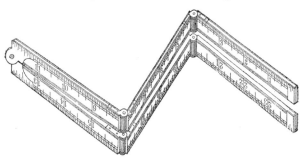

Folding Rule

We have a propensity for measurement. It gives us a sense of control and security in an uncontrollable and threatening world. We measure conduct as well as things. We measure to find proportion and balance in our lives. Propriety, prudence, civility and gracious behavior are all measured responses to life's exigencies. The craftsman, however, has more immediate goals.

"Measure twice and cut once" is the carpenter's rule. A more contemporary carpenter's rule states: "Cut to fit; beat into place." During the 19th century, the carpenter was likely to use a folding rule. These are boxwood folding rules with brass fittings. Top is Stanley No. 66 ½, a 36-inch rule. To the right is Stanley No. 54, a 24-inch rule. To the left is Lufkin, No. 372, a 12-inch rule with a 5-inch extendable caliper. Ivory versions were made and a bronze version was found in Pompeii. All were supplanted by push-pull steel measuring tapes and zigzag rules. Folding rules are a popular and specialized area for antique tool collectors.

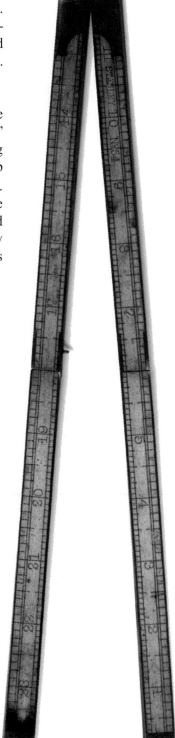

The preferred material for these rules is boxwood. Boxwood is yellow throughout and is a hard, fine-grained, durable wood that can be finely carved. It is used for chessmen and the wooden parts of hand tools. The wood was originally imported from Turkey and Persia, and later from South America. The boxwood tree grows only to a thickness of six inches and is increasingly rare.

The Stanley family formed the Stanley Company in Bristol, Connecticut, in 1852. Subsequently, the Stanley Rule and Level Company was founded and, in the 1860s, became the second largest maker of rules after Chapin-Stephens. At the time, Stanley Rule and Level Co. was manufacturing about 80 different rules. The Stanley Co. purchased Chapin-Stephens in 1929.

Folding rule - Lufkin No. 372 - 2004 - $70
Folding rule - Stanley No. 54 - 2004 - $75
Folding rule - Stanley No. 66 ½ - 2004 - $50

Micrometer Calipers

Pundits, politicians and educators have expressed "zero tolerance" for drugs, lawlessness, sexual harassment, disruptive school behavior, drunk driving and improper punctuation. Too bad, none of them have zero tolerance for hackneyed expression.

In mechanical engineering, tolerance is a permissible range of deviation from some specified dimension. As an example, 0.7 in. ± 0.005 in. For engineers and machinists, zero tolerance is a physical impossibility, a self-negating condition, an oxymoron. Specifying exact tolerances is practical only where measurements can confirm them. Historically, closer tolerances require measurements of increasing precision.

An instrument we use to measure to ten thousandths of an inch was first designed to measure planets. A micrometer counts turns of a screw thread to measure dimensions. William Gascoigne (1620-1644) invented the micrometer and combined it with a telescope to measure the apparent diameters of planets.

Henry Maudsley (1771-1831) invented the first truly accurate micrometer incorporating a calibrated screw. A prerequisite was the ability to cut a consistent and highly accurate screw thread. The accuracy of the screw thread depends on the accuracy of the lead (controlling) screw on a screw-cutting lathe. The lead screw guides the cutting bit. Henry Maudsley also invented the lead screw. He used one lead screw to cut another. He gradually increased their consistency and accuracy by packing gutta percha (a form of latex) in the lead screw follower to average out errors and inconsistencies in the threads. In effect, bootstrapping increasing accuracy.

Maudsley referred to his best micrometer as the "Lord Chancellor" because of its commanding accuracy. It could measure to one ten thousandth of an inch. It had a screw 16 inches long with 100 threads to the inch. This standard of accuracy fostered the mass production of interchangeable parts. Maudsley's work was carried on by Joseph Whitworth (1803-1887) who standardized screw threads and advanced the science of metrology (measurement) by inventing a "comparator" capable of measuring to one millionth of an inch.

Large micrometer: 3 to 4 in. capacity
J. T. Slocomb Co.
Small micrometer: 1 in. capacity
Lufkin

See "Rifle" and "Ship's Block."

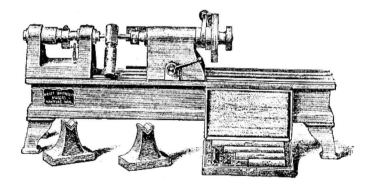

A comparator based on Whitworth's design

Micrometer - same type, quality and period - 2006 - $20

Universal Bevel Protractor

Imagine Ron Popeil manufacturing microscopes. Laroy Sunderland Starrett invented the "Hasher" (see below), a food chopper, in 1865. It sold well even though, as the name implies, it lacked the precision of his later inventions. "Every Housewife knows that it requires from 1 to 3 hours tedious labor with the common hand-knife and tray to cut the meat and apple for an ordinary batch of mince pies. With the American Chopper a child 6 years of age can do the same work in from 5 to 15 minutes with the greatest of ease." Clearly, this was before the era of child labor laws.

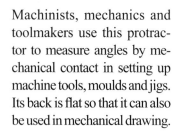

Starrett's Hasher
(American Chopper)

Starett deserted kitchen technology for machining technology. His first precision tool was a combination square with a head that could be clamped in any position along the rule. L. S. Starrett had a genius for inventing and manufacturing precision tools. He invented improvements to the screw thread gage, calipers, dividers, and micrometers. This bevel protractor was his invention of 1892.

Machinists, mechanics and toolmakers use this protractor to measure angles by mechanical contact in setting up machine tools, moulds and jigs. Its back is flat so that it can also be used in mechanical drawing.

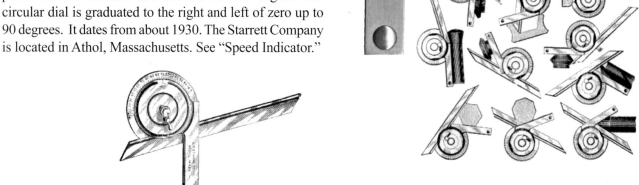

This Starrett No. 364 stainless steel protractor has a 7-inch blade and two opposing verniers. It has a locking lever, a locking thumbwheel and an acute angle attachment. This protractor can measure to 5 minutes or 1/12 degree. The circular dial is graduated to the right and left of zero up to 90 degrees. It dates from about 1930. The Starrett Company is located in Athol, Massachusetts. See "Speed Indicator."

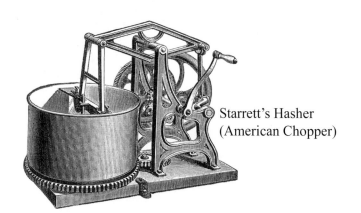

Universal bevel protractor - same type, quality and period - 2010 - $56

148

Machinists' Level

Leonard L. Davis organized the Davis Level and Tool Co. in 1868. In 1890, an admiring reporter wrote, "Mr. Davis, the founder and general business manager is a native of Laconia, N.H., a courteous and obliging gentleman, a broad-minded and liberal citizen, and a thorough-going, progressive, and a successful manufacturer and merchant." And this was *not* an obituary. Davis was an inventor as well as a level-headed entrepreneur. He was the first to include an inclinometer in his levels.

Because of its greater accuracy, millwrights and machinists use a machinists' level to install and set up engines and machine tools. Machinists' levels are steel or iron rather than wood. In a spirit level (spirit because the tube contains alcohol), the bubble tube arcs so that the bubble moves to the top center. When the center of the bubble is tangent to the top rail of the level, the level is true – "on the level." The curvature of this arc determines the sensitivity of the level. The greater the radius of this arc, then the greater the sensitivity of the level. The chambers of bubble tubes are ground to specific arcs. Bubble tubes with an arc radius of 1,200 feet have the greatest sensitivity. Modern machinists' spirit levels have an accuracy to .005 inch per foot.

This Davis Machinists' Iron Level No. 2 includes a rotatable brass inclinometer. The level is 12 in. long, 2 1/4 in. high and 7/8 in. thick. It is stamped with a patent date of Sept. 17, 1867. It looks as if it were inspired by the ornamental iron railings of the French Quarter of New Orleans.

In 1902, Montgomery Ward sold this Davis machinists' level for $2.15.

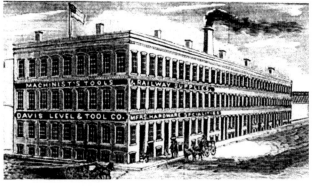

Machinist's level - same type, quality and period - 2010 - $75

149

Paint Spray Gun

"You can have any color you like, so long as it's black.", said Henry Ford referring to his famous Model T. Today's color alternatives are proposed by the Color Marketing Group, an association of color and design professionals that forecasts the annual spectrum for six consumer industries. Here are a few example colors for 2006.

"*Sweet:* Gender-bending pink asserts youth and power. This is a neo-pink for all seasons as a main color event."

"*Electric Mud:* Visual communication is stuck on this deep rich brown based on the meeting of technology and nature."

"*Georgian Bay*: Transportation balances the blue and green of both technology and organics for a fresh clean color sparked by silver fleck."

"*Orange You Glad!*: This high-energy color with glow and power embodies color depth. This fashion color offers movement and fluidity to drive consumers to say, 'I need it!'"

What would Henry think?

Another esthetic sensibility, scent, may have inspired the spray gun since it is based on the same principle as the perfume atomizer. The principle of the atomizer or spray gun is simple: air forces a liquid through a small orifice, breaking the liquid into droplets or mist. Controlling that spray and adjusting for viscosity to achieve a specific desired result is not so simple. In 1888, Dr. Allen De Vilbiss invented an atomizer for throat medications. He established the De Vilbiss Manufacturing Company, later becoming The De Vilbiss Company.

In 1907, Dr. De Vilbiss's son, Thomas, experimented with the spray gun, inventing improvements. Because of slow-drying paints and lacquers of the period, painting a car took as long as forty days. By 1910, the auto industry began to use spray guns in place of brushwork for paint application, paving the way for red candy-apple silver-flake finishes. In the 1920s, Thomas De Vilbiss broadened the company's sex appeal by introducing a successful line of luxury perfumizers (perfume atomizers). The atomizer moved from the auto factory to the olfactory. The product line expanded to air compressors and air-operated tools. Black & Decker eventually acquired the company. With all his inventiveness, Thomas De Vilbiss could not have anticipated the aerosol paint can, graffiti and the art of the tagger.

The aerosol paint can is a spin-off technology of the spray gun. Maybe some tagger or graffiti artist should acknowledge the inventiveness of Thomas De Vilbiss with a dedicated wall of respect.

With its high-quality, nickle-plated brass construction, this paint spray gun looks more like a medical instrument than an industrial tool.

Manufactured by The De Vilbiss Company, Toledo, Ohio.
American patent: Nov. 29, 1910. Canadian patent: March 7, 1911.
Type D. Serial No. 16937. Height: 8 in.

Paint spray gun - same type, quality and period - 2006 - $53

Violinmakers Molds

Italian Style

French Style

French Style

We have not yet determined whether these molds were used by Amati, Guarneri, or Stradivari. The magnificent Antonio Stradivari (1644-1737) made instruments in families and gave each family a name. In addition to violins, Stradivari made violas, cellos mandolins, harps, and guitars. A family might consist of a violin as mother, another violin as son, viola as father, cello as grandfather, and a guitar as bastard. He would try to sell the instruments altogether as a family. A recent price for a Strativari violin was $3,500,000. Referring to his own fiddle, Jack Benny said, "If this is not a Stradivari, I've been robbed of $110."

Molds provide the surfaces against which the ribs or sides of the violin are clamped as they are glued to internal blocks so that the ribs hold their shape. The two types of molds are shown here. The Italian style is an internal mold with the blocks and ribs clamped to its outside edges. The French style (two examples) are external molds with the ribs and blocks clamped to the inside edges of the mold. Traditionally, the top or belly of the violin is spruce and the back, neck, and ribs are maple. Carved compound curves form the belly, back, and neck. Strips of maple bent into shape with a hot iron form the ribs.

These molds do not have the finish one would expect in clamping molds used in the factory production of instruments. The rectangular holes in the external mold where clamps are placed were cut by a hand chisel and not by a powered mortising tool. Crisp, regular, up-and-down saw marks (not slanted or curved) on the same mold suggest wood cut by a vertical saw mill, possibly before the general introduction of circular saws in about 1860. Most likely, an individual craftsman made these molds for his own use as a violin maker.

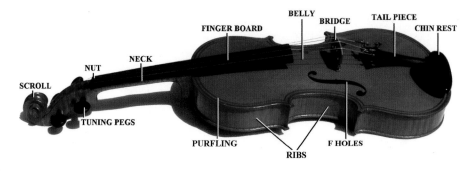

151

Plumb Bob

Plumb (from Latin for "lead") means true and straight. The plumb bob and line may be the simplest of all construction tools. Before the spirit level, small plumb bobs with cords were attached to an A frame or square to set true horizontal lines as well as vertical lines. The Egyptians used such devices as early as 2600 BC. For surveying, the ancient Romans used a kind of staff from which five plumb bobs were suspended. What are plumb bobs made of? Almost anything subject to the force of gravity. The Egyptians used egg-shaped stones. Some plumb bobs were lead (as the name implies). Later plumb bobs are brass, steel, cast iron, or combinations of wood and iron. They may be painted, or nickel or chrome plated. Some plumb bobs contain a reservoir for mercury to dampen their oscillation and others, made of brass, have replaceable steel tips. Some plumb bobs include an integral reel for the plumb line, a little like a yoyo. A plummet-lamp is a plumb bob incorporating a light that is used in mining and tunnel surveys (it should have been called a "lightweight"). The more prized plumb bobs have fitted wooden cases.

Some ancient genius observed that truly vertical walls stand up while tilted walls fall down. So, a major use of plumb bobs is as a reference in checking the verticality of walls and framing in construction. Another use is to transfer a reference point from one level or elevation to another. In surveying, plumb bobs were used to locate the surveyor's level or theodolite directly over the station mark and to locate points in using a measuring tape.

For many applications, the plumb bob and spirit level have been displaced by laser devices that project a reference dot or line on surfaces or sensors.

Galileo

For buildings out-of-plumb, a plumb bob would show that the Leaning Tower of Pisa takes the prize. It has a tilt of 5.5 degrees with its top gallery 15 feet from vertical. Engineers expect to reduce this tilt by drilling out soil from underneath the foundation on the high side of the Tower. The Tower, famed because it resists the force of gravity, also served as a stage for Galileo's gravity experiment. According to legend, he simultaneously dropped five-pound and ten-pound cannonballs from the Tower, demonstrating that objects fall with the same acceleration regardless of weight. In doing so, he disproved Aristotle's assertion that objects fall at different rates proportional to their weight. A corollary to Newton's laws of gravity states that "an attempt to save a fragile falling body will produce more damage than if the attempt had not been made."

Patternmakers Sculpting Tools

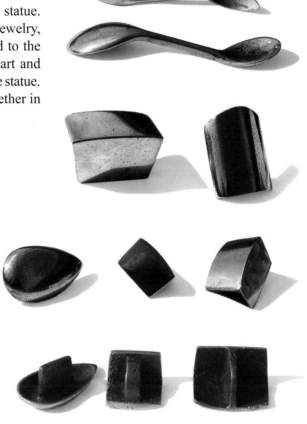

Unlucky in love? Can't find Mister Right or Miss Right? Take a tip from Pygmalion: create a mate.

Spurned by an unfaithful lover, the sculptor Pygmalion became disenchanted with real women and carved an ideal woman of ivory. Then, he fell passionately in love with his statue. Though he adorned her with fine clothes and costly jewelry, she proved unresponsive. In desperation, he appealed to the goddess Aphrodite. Aphrodite admired Pygmalion's art and pitied him for his unrequited love. She granted life to the statue. The maiden married Pygmalion and the two lived together in perfect harmony until they got to know each other.

If Pygmalion had been a patternmaker, he could have created a whole chorus line of ideal women. The patternmakers repertoire of skills includes cutting, shaping and forming patterns for molds and making templates, models and prototypes. He works in wood, plastic, metal, plaster or clay, but not ivory. He used these tools for sculpting in clay or plaster. At one time, tools such as these would be used to sculpt Detroit's latest prototype auto. Molders would use these same tools in finishing casting molds.

CAD (computer assisted design) in combination with CAM (computer assisted machining) have relegated most of the patternmaker's skills to the industrial scrap heap. CAD programs operate computerized milling machines to produce almost any shape out of a very wide range of materials. As an additional advantage, scaling is accomplished reliably and automatically.

These sculpting tools are cast brass. The longest is 11 in. in length. The shorter tools have a projection in the back, as you can see in the lower row. These projections serve as grips for using the tool.

See "Bevel Gear Casting Pattern."

Set of sculpting tools - same type, quality and period - 2004 - $75

Blowtorch

Not hot enough to weld, but easily hot enough for lead soldering, thawing pipes and stripping paint, the blowtorch was a standard tool of the plumber and handyman. This is a brass, gasoline-fueled blowtorch. The first working blowtorches were manufactured in Sweden in about 1880.

In operation, the pump pressurizes gasoline in the tank. The black drip tray below the burner head holds a quantity of gasoline which is ignited to heat the burner. When the burner head is hot, the valve is opened admitting gasoline through a wick tube and passed a check valve. There is a small channel between the check valve and the nozzle where the gasoline heats up and vaporizes. The vaporized gasoline, now under considerable pressure, is forced through the nozzle where it ignites. The pressurized burning gasoline vapor provides the "blow" of the blowtorch and its characteristic roar.

Suppose you were firing up a gasoline blowtorch. You didn't put enough gasoline in the drip tray and the burner head is not hot enough to vaporize the gasoline. You open the valve and a two-foot stream of burning gasoline shoots from the nozzle. What you've got is a flamethrower. Not really what you wanted. Suppose you used the pressure pump while the torch is operating, a no-no. Because of a slightly leaky gasket, the whole torch is enveloped in burning gasoline. Not really what you wanted. If the valves, seals, gaskets or tank are leaky, you've got burning gasoline all over the place. Not really what you wanted. No wonder the propane torch displaced the gasoline blowtorch. It proved just as effective, safer and more convenient. Besides, the propane torch makes a better crème brûlée.

Manufactured in about 1920. Within an embossed shield on front:

Clayton & Lambert Mfg. Co.
Trade Mark
Made in U.S.A.

Height: 11 in. Diameter: 5 1/2 in.

Founded in Michigan in 1882 by the Lambert brothers, Clayton & Lambert manufactured blowtorches and firepots for melting lead. In 1899, the Company built a plant in Detroit and subsequently moved to Kentucky. The Company produced metal stampings for the auto industry and cartridge cases during war time. It manufactured its last blowtorch in 1970 as plastic piping displaced copper and steel piping in plumbing systems.

Gasoline blowtorch - same type, quality and period 2004 - $25

Tufting Tool

In your daydream you discover that you are distantly related to royalty and entitled to a coat of arms. To celebrate this new dignity, you order a carpet bearing your coat of arms for the living room floor, a common practice for royalty. Using current technology, this "armorial carpet" with its unique design would be tufted with an electric or pneumatic tufting tool. The tool you see here is its precursor.

The process of creating a pile surface of looped yarn inserted into a fabric backing is ancient. Coptic mats from the sixth century employ this technique. Hooked rugs employ a closely related process. Hand tufting of bedspreads and small rugs developed as a women's cottage industry around Dalton, Georgia, in the 1890's. About 1922, tufting machines were invented and in 1949 these were adapted to produce broadloom carpeting.

Tufted loop pile and backing

Imagine a sewing machine 12 feet wide with 1,200 needles all operating at the same time. This is, in effect, the machine on which broadloom tufted carpets are produced. Tufted rugs have taken over the market for rugs such as Wilton and Axeminster. They have the broadloom market all sewn up. Electric or pneumatic-powered hand-held tufting tools are currently used to produce one-of-a-kind designs (family crests and logos) in tufted carpets.

This tool inserts yarn into a canvas backing to create a looped pile. A hollow needle carries the yarn through the backing. The stitch length and loop height are adjustable. A frame holds the canvas and stretches it taut. The tufter, working from the back, follows a pattern stenciled or drawn on the canvas.

The tool is made of nickel-plated steel. Length: 11 in. The tool carries a patent date of April 13, 1888, but no manufacturer's name.

If the tool were stamped "By appointment, tufter to His Majesty, Edward VII, King of England", it would have been worth a great deal more.

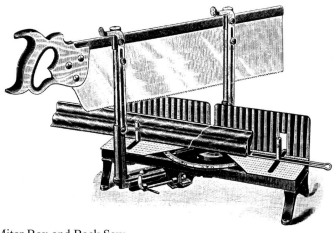

Miter Box and Back Saw

The miter box holds a work piece while making accurate angled cuts. The back saw has a fold of steel or brass opposite the cutting edge to increase the blade's rigidity. The miter box and back saw are used in cutting molding, in making frames and in cabinetry. Although still in use, it is largely displaced by the mitering power saw (chop saw).

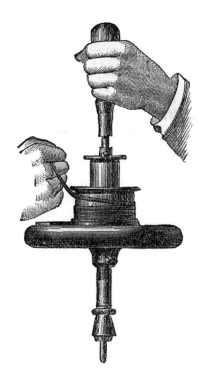

Hand Drill

With an action similar to a bow drill, this drill was spring-loaded so it re-wound the string after it was pulled. See "Bitstock."

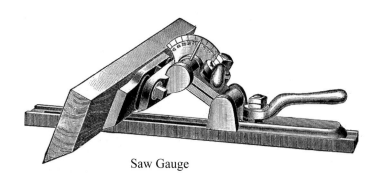

Saw Gauge

This gauge measured the angle of the cutting blade and was used before an angle gauge was made integral with the saw.

Boring Machine

This boring machine was a precursor to the drill press. It could bore at almost any angle and had adjustable depth stops. See "Bitstock."

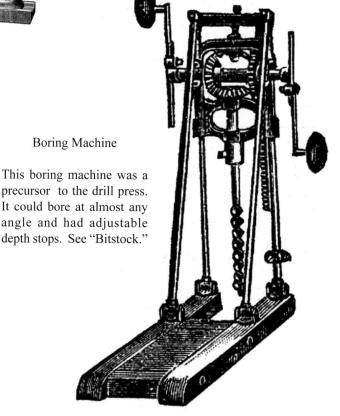

Wrench

This wrench of 1873 could grasp nuts and pipes. The wood handle is a touch of elegance lacking in modern wrenches.

A few more examples of tool technology

Combination Tool

This tool combined a drill, anvil, vise, pipe vise and hardy (cut-off tool). It lacks a clock-radio, but was a bargain amalgam of shop tools for its day (about 1900).

Combination Scroll Saw and Lathe

This foot-powered combination scroll saw and wood lathe (below) was not recommended for the professional; a tacit admission that combination tools may lack the performance of their single-function counterparts.

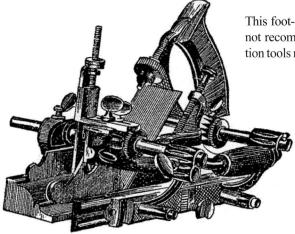

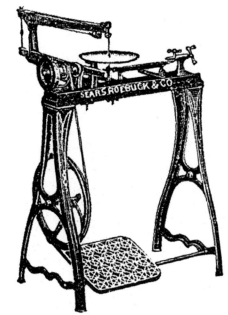

Universal Plane

This plane included cutters for molding, chamfering, beading, reeding, fluting, plowing, dadoing, rabbeting, filistering, slitting and more. It is highly-prized by tool collectors as a working, multi-function tool.

Corner Brace

The corner brace sounds about as plausible as the proverbial left-handed monkey wrench, but it was useful and examples are fairly common. In this illustration, the second (or driven) gear is shown in a cutaway view.

Tool technology update

The 20th century saw the introduction of electric and pneumatic power tools and the automation of the production line. The result of these tool technologies: collapsing production costs and exploding production volume for virtually all manufactured consumer goods. The tool and tool operator are becoming one and the same due to 21st-century robotics. Robotics will dominate 21st-century production and, possibly, 21st-century life styles.

Karl Capek, a Czech playwright, coined the word "robot" in his 1921 play. It derives from the Czech word for "work." The U.S. Census Bureau offers a long-winded definition of robot, "a reprogrammable multifunctional manipulator designed to move material, parts, tools or specialized devices through variable programmed motions for the performance of a variety of tasks." It is appropriate that the Census Bureau defines robots because their numbers are important and growing.

In 2004, there were at least 800,000 industrial robots worldwide. There were about 320 industrial robots per 10,000 employees in Japan, in Germany 148 robots per 10,000 employees and in the United States 60 robots per 10,000 employees. The number of industrial robots alone will exceed one million by 2007. Robots are rapidly expanding into other human activities.

These are the data for 2003:

> Professional service robots for use in underwater systems, laboratories, cleaning, demolition and construction, medicine, security and agriculture - 610,000 robots.

> Personal service robots for domestic tasks, education and training, transportation, leisure and entertainment - 700,000 robots.

Remember C3PO of *Star Wars*? It was a public relations robot. According to the United Nations Economic Commission for Europe, 15 public relations robots actually exist. There is no description of their duties. Presumably, they answer phones and assure the caller his message is important.

With booming robot development and production, the looming economic dilemma is obvious. Who will buy products and services when wage-earning workers are displaced by robots? In the conclusion of Karl Capek's play, the robots turned into humans. A more probable scenario is the invention of robotic consumers.

9 ON THE JOB

Camera
Miner's safety lamp
Carbide lamp
Grain probe
Milk testing centrifuge
Letter copying press
Typewriter
Firehose nozzle
Torsion balance
Caboose air whistle
Traveler
Beer tap
Dough thermometer
Steelyard
Watchmaker's lathe
Glass cutter
Thread counter
Job stick
Buggy whip

Danny McGooty treasures his work more than most — "When I realized that what I had turned out to be was a lousy, two-bit pool hustler and drunk, I wasn't depressed at all. I was glad to have a profession."

We associate certain objects with different trades and professions. For example: a cue is to a pool hustler as a typewriter is to a secretary as a camera is to a photographer as a wrench is to a mechanic as a red light is to a... well, you get the idea. In this section, we look at obsolete technology used in specific lines of work. These include the miner, brakeman, wheelwright, baker, bartender, apothecary, typesetter, coachman and scrivener, among others.

How many lines of work are there? The *Dictionary of Occupational Titles* includes 12,000 job descriptions. Here are a few occupational titles, implausible, but true. Guess what these workers do.

Wafer breaker
Lumpia wrapper maker
Skoog machine operator
Zanjero
Polysomnography technician
Top waddy
Sponger
Wink-cutter operator
Upsetter setter-up
Tin-whiz machine operator

Next page for the answers.

Occupational Technology Time Line

Approximate Year of Manufacture of Objects in this Chapter		Year of Significant Events
	1815	Miner's safety lamp invented
	1839	Daguerrotype invented
	1868	Airbrake invented
Traveler	1875	
Camera	1880	Employee time clock invented
Letter copying press	1890	
Miner's safety lamp	1890	
Torsion balance	1891	
Glass cutter	1895	
Buggy whip	1897	Workmen's compensation passed
	1901	Electric typewriter invented
Firehose nozzle	1906	
Milk testing centrifuge	1907	
Carbide lamp	1908	
Typewriter	1913	
Dough thermometer	1920	
Steelyard	1920	
Watchmaker's lathe	1920	
Grain probe	1930	
Caboose air whistle	1932	
Job stick	1935	Unemployment insurance passed

Wafer breaker - breaks semiconductor wafers into individual dies

Lumpia wrapper maker - prepares wraps for Philippine specialty foods

Skoog machine operator - cuts and inserts plugs to correct plywood or veneer defects

Zanjero - controls irrigation systems

Polysomnography technician - measures electrical activity of the brain in those with sleep disorders

Top waddy - supervises cowboys

Sponger - smooths edges of ceramics before firing

Wink-cutter operator - operates machine to extrude and cut cured rubber

Upsetter setter-up - sets up forging machines

Tin-whiz machine operator - coats silk or rayon fabric with a tin solution

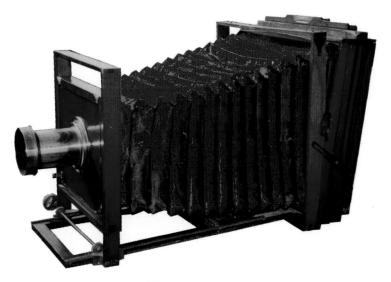

Camera

Why does great, great grandfather look so grim? Say "cheese"...keep saying "cheese"...keep saying "cheese"... keep saying "cheese"... for up to ten minutes. Depending on the process, posing for a photographic portrait required plenty of patience in the early nineteenth century. The photographer used special brackets concealed behind the subject to hold the head still. The strain of this unnatural immobility accounts for the universally frowning faces in early photographic portraiture.

Year	Process	Exposure time under optimum conditions
1839	Daguerrotype	30 minutes
1841	Calotype	3 minutes
1850	Collodion	10 seconds
1864	Collodian emulsion	15 seconds
1879	Rapid gelatin emulsion	1/15th second

This bellows full-plate camera has a frame of mahogany with brass fittings. The bellows is rubberized fabric. Several breaks in the frame have been repaired. Rack and pinion focusing on a front piece rack. Lens housing maximum diameter: 3 1/4 in. Camera length extended: 24 in. Height: 15 in. Width: 14 in. Third quarter 19th century.

Engraved on lens housing: **10x12 "IMPERIAL"**
Rapid Rectilinear
No 394
Sweet Wallach & Co.
Sole agents Chicago

J. H. Dallmeyer invented the Rapid Rectilinear lens in 1868. It produced greater marginal clarity and sharper focus for general purpose photography than prior lenses.

Rapid Rectilinear Lens.

Cameras - same type, quality and period
1999 - $350

Miner's Safety Lamp

Would you prefer Aladdin's lamp, the lamp of Diogenes or a Davy lamp? The Davy lamp is the only one that works. It saved the lives of countless canaries and thousands of miners.

Explosive gas or air with too little oxygen often threatened the miner's life. To check for oxygen, a caged canary was taken into the mine. When it dropped from its perch, the miner was at risk. Explosive gas (called "fire damp") ignited by miners' lamps was a frequent and fatal hazard. In 1815, Humphry Davy, a British chemist, developed a lamp that drew oxygen from the atmosphere without igniting surrounding explosive gas and it revealed dangerously low oxygen when the flame burned blue. He sought neither patent nor monetary reward for his invention. For his noble contribution, he received a title of nobility and the gratitude of miners.

Humphry Davy

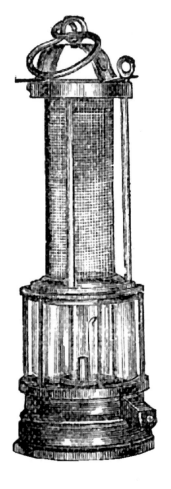

Davy's lamp was first used at the Hebburn Colliery on January 9, 1816. Its light permitted deep seams to be mined despite the presence of flammable gases.

This is a heavy brass and steel oil lamp with a flintwheel igniter next to the wick. It uses the design of Sir Humphry Davy, a combination of internal screens of brass wire mesh that cool combustion gas as it escapes so it cannot ignite explosive gas. This lamp was made in the last quarter of the 19th century.

Height: 11 1/2 in. Diameter: 31/2 in.

The brass plaque on the base of the lamp reads:

Wolf Safety Lamp Co of America Inc New York U.S.A.

This lamp is a symbol of safety to the miner as the life preserver is to the sailor. Though timeworn, its sturdy construction still protects it from the rattle of pick axe and falling rock. It exhibits excellent industrial functional design.

See "Miner's Carbide Light" and "Masthead Light."

Davy lamp - same type, quality and period - 1977 - $20, 2005 - $175

Miner's Carbide Lamp

It's dark as a dungeon and damp as the dew,
Where the dangers are double and the pleasures are few,
Where the rain never falls and the sun never shines,
It's dark as a dungeon down in the mines.

From the folk song, *Dark as a Dungeon Down in the Mines*

The verse is an understatement. At the end of the nineteenth century, the accident rate in mines was not double, but five times the accident rate above ground. One of the few pleasures might be a Cornish pasty for lunch. Circumstances permitting, the miner would warm the pasty on the blade of his shovel held over a fire.

For fifty years spanning the turn of the century, miners dispelled the darkness with carbide lamps. Calcium carbide is a compound of carbon and calcium. When mixed with water, it produces acetylene, a highly flammable and brilliantly burning gas. Carbide came into use near the end of the 19th century with the appropriate burner nozzle design and an understanding of safe handling. The traditional miner's hard hat had a carbide lamp fixed to it.

This lamp is made of heavy tinned steel with a turned oak handle. No maker's marks. The thumb screw on top forces the lid down for an airtight seal of the chamber where carbide mixes with water to produce acetylene. The lens and reflector slide off to expose the burner nozzle to ignite the gas.

Height: 10 1/2 in.
Diameter of base: 3 3/4 in.

Brass plaque on back reads: REGD No. 878136
                                FORMERLY 686127
                                FILL TO

←——————————→

                                THIS MARK

KA-POP or KA-BOOM – the sound of acetylene exploding. If gaskets or seals were not intact, acetylene could escape and ignite. If the burner nozzle orifice was blocked, the whole lamp could explode. Where a Davy lamp might prevent explosions, a carbide lamp could cause one. Acetylene does have one redeeming safety feature: it stinks. Here is part of the manufacturer's instructions for operating the "Demon Strike Light" carbide lamp:

> *To light, cover the Reflector with palm of hand, hold a few seconds, then draw the hand downwards quickly, rubbing the hand over the wheel, making a spark which lights the gas. If hand is held too long, a loud report is produced but does no harm.*

See "Miner's Safety Lamp" and "Masthead Light."

Miner's carbide lamps - same type, quality and period
1977 $12
1999 $185

Grain Probe

This device helped to halt witch hunts. The grain probe is used to sample grain. Grain is sampled primarily to find evidence of insect infestation and mold. The most common poisonous grain mold is *aspergillus flavus,* producing aflatoxin which causes liver cancer. A rare, but more interesting mold is *claviceps purpura,* producing ergot alkaloids closely related to LSD. Consuming ergot alkaloids has hellish consequences.

December, 1691, Salem Village, Massachusetts. Eight girls afflicted with disordered speech, odd postures, gestures and convulsive fits claim bewitchment. The girls complain of choking, pin pricking and pinching sensations, vomiting and apparitions. They identify both poor, eccentric, and respectable members of their community as persecutors. Of these accused witches, 20 are hanged or crushed to death, all protesting their innocence. Cotton Mather was a minister of Boston's Old North Church and an instigator of these witch trials.

According to the researches of Linda R. Caporael, the girls display the clinical symptoms of ergot poisoning. Rye was a staple of the residents of Salem Village. The mold grows on rye, especially in warm wet weather. These were the conditions around Salem Village in the summer of 1691 when the rye was harvested. Since ergot poisoning was unknown in Massachusetts, the symptoms were explained as Satanic possession invoked by witchcraft, a notion entirely compatible with Puritan beliefs.

Caporael concludes that the Salem witchcraft trials and executions were the tragic result of the conflux of a disease unknown to the community and religious superstitions. Historical evidence suggests that some European witchcraft persecutions may also be explained by outbreaks of ergot poisoning. Mathew Hopkins was a witch hunter in England in the 1640s. He identified witches by casting them in rivers. If they floated, they were guilty. In Essex alone, he hung as many as 60 accused in one year. In 1647 he was, himself accused, cast into a river and floated. So, he was hung as a wizard — a witch hunter hoist with his own petard, a fate escaped by Cotton Mather.

The grain elevator operator or miller used this probe to extract grain samples. It is shown here partially open. Turning the knob at the top opens or closes the chamber. The probe is closed and inserted in the grain pile, then the knob is turned to open the chamber. The grain flows in and the chamber is closed and the probe withdrawn.

All brass with bronze tip.

Length: 40 in. Diameter at tip: 1 1/2 in.

Burrows Equipment Company

Evanston, Illinois

Cotton Mather

Grain probe - same type, quality and period - 2004 - $100

Milk Testing Centrifuge

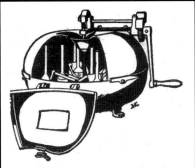

Can You Pick Out Your Best Cow?

Two cows that look equally good may not be equally profitable. It's just plain business to know your cows. Make each one, show a clear profit over feed and care, or send her to the butcher.

20th Century Hand Milk Tester

is the finest hand power milk tester made. It shows quickly and accurately the butter value of each cow's milk. If you keep cows for profit you ought to have a tester. One poor cow will easily rob you of more than the cost of the tester every year. Write today for circular giving sizes and prices of this and other milk testing apparatus. Agents wanted.

CORNISH, CURTIS & GREENE MFG. CO.,
FORT ATKINSON, WISCONSIN

Courtesy of Cornish, Curtis & Greene Mfg. Co.

In 1895 Gelett Burgess wrote a quatrain on the Purple Cow.

I never saw a purple cow.
I never hope to see one;
But, I can tell you, anyhow,
I'd rather see than be one.

This bit of doggerel was an instant success. But, entrepreneurs missed the chance to market purple milk and purple butter.

Butter is the true crème de la crème. Butter-philia antedated cholesterol-phobia. Butter fat was prized in milk and cream. Farmers wanted to breed cows that produced more butter fat. Dairy product makers and distributors wanted to buy milk containing more butter fat. The Jersey breed of cows produces milk with the highest butter fat, as high as 5.2%. Lucinda, the world's champion milk cow hails from Wisconsin and produced 67,914 pounds of milk in one year. Holy cow! That's a lot of milk. Sadly, lactating Lucinda never received the popular recognition accorded the Purple Cow.

Beginning in the late 19th century, dairymen used centrifuges of various designs to determine the butter fat content of milk samples. These may be termed "butyrometers." With a shape seemingly inspired by a pumpkin, this heavy cast iron centrifuge contains a four-armed spinner carrying eight brass baskets holding graduated glass sample bottles. The advertisement on the left is from a February 8, 1907 issue of *Hoard's Dairyman*.

Cast in relief on the door: 20TH CENTURY TESTER

Diameter: 17 in. Height: 12 1/4 in. Weight: 48 lbs.

Milk testing centrifuge - same type, quality and period - 2006 - $500

Letter Copying Press

A victim of scrivener's palsy has painful spasms of the muscles of the hand, more familiar to you as writer's cramp. A scrivener is a copy clerk or copyist, a man who functioned as the office copy machine. Bob Crachit was one such. Copy clerks were fixtures of the 19th-century office along with this letter copying press. Since there was no contemporary diagnosis of repetitive strain injury, the letter copying press was the sole relief for scrivener's palsy.

A letter copying press, used only for outgoing correspondence, could make individual copies on separate sheets or make copies in a bound copy book. The writer used special copying ink in writing a letter to be copied. The copyist would make up a sandwich of a sheet of oiled paper, the original letter, a lightly moistened sheet of translucent copy tissue and another sheet of oiled paper. The oiled papers contained the moisture. He would tighten these sheets in the letter copying press for several minutes. Under pressure, the ink from the original would transfer to the moistened tissue and penetrate it. Because of its thinness and translucence, the copy could be read from the reverse side of the tissue. A copy book was a book of bound copying tissues into which original letters and oiled paper could be interleaved and then pressed to make copies.

In 1890, John Monash, a distinguished Australian army officer and engineer, wrote a paper entitled, "The Superintendence of Contracts." Here is an excerpt. "The Letter Copy Press Book is still another expedient in the same direction. It may seem a cumbersome rule to lay down, that every paper which bears his signature a copy must be kept. It is dangerous to incur the risk of being confronted with one's own letter, the contents of which are only dimly remembered, or, perhaps, its existence entirely forgotten. The slip-shod habit of saving a few seconds that it requires to press a copy of a letter will certainly be regretted before many days have passed." As a man of integrity, John Monash kept a copy of his paper.

Some copying letter presses have scrolling floral motifs cast into the frame and others have enameled and gold leaf ornamentation. This cast iron example is strictly functional. It is a great deal heavier than carbon paper.

Length: 19 in. Width: 12 1/2 in. Height closed: 15 in.

Letter copying press - same type, quality and period - 2004 - $106

166

Typewriter

This is a Hammond Multiplex typewriter. According to the *Weekly World News* of February 13, 1996, a phantom typist favored an early Hammond Multiplex typewriter. The haunted Hammond, typing without human agency, offered post mortem messages. Although these messages lacked profundity or solid data about the afterlife, they were reassuring. The keys on these old typewriters are hard to punch, raising the specter of ectoplasmic carpal tunnel syndrome. An investigating scientist, Dr. Verstin, was stumped by the phenomenon (the typing, not the disease). Could there be spirit-operated antique vacuum cleaners? Does your dishwasher make a hollow rapping sound?

The IBM bouncing ball and this Hammond Multiplex typewriter had something in common; they were both single-element machines. The type is all on the same surface rather than distributed and fixed to multiple levers. The Hammond Multiplex carried the font on hard-rubber strips affixed to interchangeable shuttles. A wide variety of fonts were available on these shuttles, so Hammond could proudly boast "For all nations and all tongues" on its logo. This is the first model of the "Multiplex," so-called because two fonts could be fixed to the same shuttle and either font selected by rotating the shuttle.

The Hammond typewriter was first manufactured in 1884. These machines had a semicircular keyboard. The Multiplex with straight keyboard was introduced in 1913. In 1927, Hammond changed its name to Varityper and remained in business with this name until 1980 when it, too, became a victim of computer technology.

This Hammond Multiplex typewriter has an oak base and a molded oak cover. Most metal parts are nickel plated. Dimensions (typewriter proper):

        Height: 6 3/4 in.
        Width: 13 in.
        Depth: 12 3/4 in.

Hammond Multiplex Typewriter - same type, quality and period - 2003 - $100

Firehose Nozzle

Does San Francisco possess a towering firehose nozzle? San Francisco's highest hill is Telegraph Hill. Coit Tower sits on top of that hill, a 210-foot column. It is named after Lillie Coit. As a little girl, Lillie was playing in a construction site with two companions when the building caught fire. A member of Knickerbocker Engine Company Number Five rescued Lillie. Her two companions lost their lives.

Lillie became a fire fighting enthusiast and the informal mascot of Company Number Five. As a young women, she married millionaire Henry Coit. She inherited his wealth. When she died, she bequeathed a portion of her estate to build a bronze statue of firefighters in San Francisco's Washington Square. Her bequest also funded the construction of Coit Tower on Telegraph Hill. Many believe the tower was meant to suggest a firehose nozzle, but the architect denies it.

This brass firehose nozzle has a controllable valve and is wrapped in red cord to provide a better gripping surface. A good gripping surface is important because of Newton's Third Law of Motion: to every action there is an equal and contrary reaction. The reactive force at a firehose nozzle can exceed 250 lbs. This force can be lethal to firefighters if they lose control of the nozzle and it whips around. For naval firefighters, a nozzle without a valve is known as a "suicide nozzle."

Brass firehose nozzle with valve
Height: 33 1/2 in.
Diameter across nozzle tip: 1 1/2 in.
Diameter across coupling ring: 3 1/2 in.

On the coupling ring: W.D. ALLEN MFG. CO.

In 1906, the W.D. Allen Mfg. Co. of Chicago manufactured all kinds of fire fighting equipment, including hoses, firemen's helmets, hats and coats, pumps and hand-operated village fire engines.

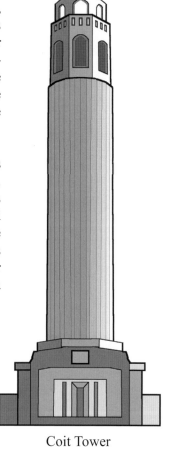

Coit Tower

Firehose nozzle - same type, quality and period - 2003 - $150

Torsion Balance

Despite the proverbial heavy thumb of the butcher, we associate balances with morality. The scales of justice suggest a true measure of right and wrong. In his vision, Belshazzar read a moral indictment: "Thou art weighed in the balance and found wanting." The astrological sign of Libra, a hanging balance, derives from an ancient Persian belief that, at the end of time, one's evil will be weighed against one's good in a great balance. A scruple is an apothecaries' measure of weight and a moral doubt or slight hesitation. Both are quite small and stem from the Latin for a little pebble. A scrupulous butcher would keep his thumb out of the weighing pan.

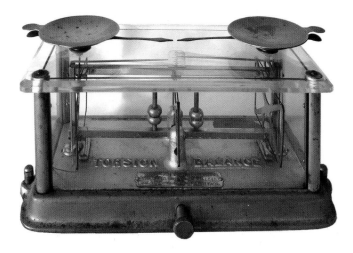

The torsion balance is interesting because it has no pivots and no bearings. The parallel double beam is suspended by three bands of strap steel. The bands twist slightly as the beam moves. Due to this arrangement, there are no friction-producing bearing surfaces. There is only internal friction within the steel bands.

This torsion balance is an apothecaries' or pharmacist's balance. The balance has a beveled-glass case and a nickel-plated cast iron base, leveling screws and beam lock. There are two compensating weights for fine calibrating adjustments. It has two nickel-plated brass pans. One of the torsion bands is broken.

Length: 10 in. Height: 5 in. Width: 5 in.

About 1891.

Plaque on base reads: The Torsion Balance Co.
                          Style 270 New York No. 11545
                          Pat. Jan. 6-85, Jan. 22-89, May 19-91.

Because of its great sensitivity, torsion (twisting) in a strap or wire has been used in scientific research to measure the gravitational attraction between two masses and the attractive force of an electric charge. Contemporary balances can measure to a millionth of a gram. Common electronic analytical balances weigh to one ten thousands of a gram. Any balance that is less accurate than one gram is considered a scale.

See "Analytical Balance" and "Steelyard."

Torsion balances - same type, quality and period -
1977 - $32
1999 - $200

Apothecaries' weights

Caboose Air Whistle

When trains were slower, trips longer, and train crews larger, the caboose served as a rolling home for the crew. It also served as an office for the conductor. The box with windows on top of the caboose, the cupola or lookout, was used by the conductor to spot problems with the train. He looked for freight cars trailing smoke. The smoke signaled a hot box where wheel bearings had overheated. In the early 1800's, the earliest cabooses were shanties on flatcars. Then, boxcars were converted to cabooses. The cupola was added in the 1870s.

The word "caboose" probably derives from a Dutch word for ship's galley, *kabuis*. Another possible origin is the Americanized Spanish word for jail house, *calaboose*. Railroad slang for the caboose was "crummy," "bone-braker," "doghouse," and "hearse." A short, four-wheeled caboose was called a "bobber." Railroad management referred to the caboose as a "way car."

The caboose air whistle was located on the rear platform of a caboose. A brakeman blew the whistle when the caboose backed over a crossing. Compressed air for the air brakes powered the whistle. The whistle included a valve used to apply air brakes in an emergency.

The Sherburne Co. of Boston, Massachusetts, manufactured this brass whistle and valve. The patent number, 1890212, dates it to about 1932. In this same year, the United States was in the depths of the Great Depression. Thousands of unemployed men, looking for work, bummed rides in empty boxcars or "blinds." If they couldn't get into a boxcar, they would ride the "rods," metal trusses under the boxcars and a hazardous location. The sound of this air whistle would have been familiar to them as trains backed through railroad yards and into terminals. A folk song of the times mentions Jay Gould, owner of the Erie and Union Pacific Railroads and a robber baron.

> Jay Gould's daughter said before she died,
> "Daddy, fix the blinds so the bums can't ride.
> If ride they must, let them ride the rods.
> Let them put their trust in the hands of God."

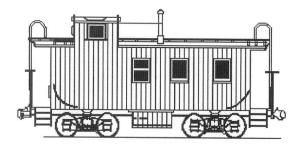
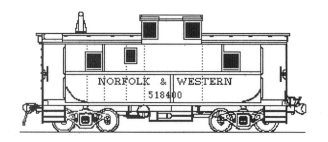

Caboose air whistle - same type, quality and period - 2004 - $40

Traveler

Every day, Helios with radiant face, illuminates the world by driving his chariot from east to west. With due reverence to the ancient Greeks, we can subject this explanation of day and night to the test of archaeology. Since the spoked wheel was not invented until 2,000 B.C., we must assume some other mechanism for day and night prior to that date.

A chariot wheel or wooden wagon wheel begins at the hub with mortised holes to receive the spokes. The wheelwright carves and inserts the spokes so that the wheel is slightly dished. A felloe is a wooden wheel rim segment. Felloes are fitted to the spokes and doweled together end-to-end to make the wooden wheel rim.

A traveler is a measuring tool used by a wheelwright to find the perimeter of the wheel. The perimeter is the length of the steel strap needed to make the tire for the wheel. The wheelwright rolls the traveler along the edge of the wheel and chalk-marks the wheel after each complete rotation of the traveler. The number of rotations times the circumference of the traveler plus any remaining segment equals the perimeter of the wheel. Many travelers have an inch rule calibrated along the edge and this is used to measure the length of any final segment.

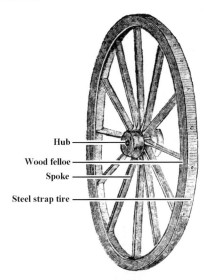

Hub
Wood felloe
Spoke
Steel strap tire

Either a blacksmith or wheelwright cuts the steel tire strap to a length slightly shorter than that measured by the traveler, bends it into a circle and forge-welds the ends together. The tire is heated until it is red hot and expands slightly. Then, it is forced over the wooden rim of the wheel and the wheel is plunged into water. When the steel tire cools and contracts, it pulls the wheel together with tremendous force. To the right, you see wheelwrights forcing the burning hot tire strap over the wheel rim. Could this work of the wheelwright have suggested the wheel of fire in Ezekiel's vision, or was it the chariot wheels of Helios rolling through the sky?

This traveler is cast iron with serpentine spokes and brass pointer. It has a twenty-four inch rule with fractional graduations along the wheel edge. Manufactured about 1875.

Overall length: 13 3/4 in. Diameter of wheel: 7 3/4 in.

Traveler - same type, quality and period - 2005 - $80

171

Beer Tap

"Not all chemicals are bad. Without chemicals such as hydrogen and oxygen, for example, there would be no way to make water, a vital ingredient in beer." Dave Barry.

Other ingredients include malted barley, hops and yeast. Barley, the hardiest of all cereals, provides the base. Malting is a process of germinating and cooking the barley. Hops preserve and flavor the brew. Fruit or syrups may also be added as flavoring. Yeast is added to the malted barley mash or "wort." Top fermenting yeast produces ale. Bottom fermenting yeast produces lager. Strictly speaking, both ale and lager are beer. Ale usually has a stronger flavor than lager.

The Summerians of about 6000 BC first brewed beer. They worshipped a goddess of brewing, *Ninkasi.* A hymn to the goddess includes complete instructions for brewing beer. King Gambrinus, the putative patron saint of brewing, has a beer named after him. Why not a beer named "Ninkasi", honoring the gracious goddess of brewing? Gilgamesh would endorse it.

Beer tap handles are collectibles in their own right, especially those with names and logos of popular brands. This beer tap is meant for heavy usage. The Cleveland Manufacturing Company manufactured it from cast and turned brass. Height from tip of handle to bottom of spout: 13 in.

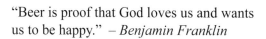

Barley

Hops

"Beer is proof that God loves us and wants us to be happy." – *Benjamin Franklin*

"Here's mud in your eye!" What does *that* mean? The toast probably derives from the horsey set. In a horse race, the jockey on the following horse is likely to get spattered with mud. So, the toast expresses the irritatingly competitive sentiment — may my horse beat your horse. Belly up to the bar while the bartender pulls the tap handle and fills your stein. If it's a pale lager, the temperature should be between 45° to 50° F. Ales and dark lagers should be served at 50° to 55° F. The typical beer is about 4.5 percent alcohol by volume. The Boston Beer Company produced beer as high as 24 percent alcohol by volume. That amounts to 48 proof. A couple of steins of this beer and you'll need a designated walker.

Gambrinus

See "Alembic" and "Hydrometer."   Beer tap - same type, quality and period - 2005 - $69

Dough Thermometer

OUCH! The baker had his ear nailed to his shop doorpost. That was the punishment for selling adulterated bread in 18th-century Turkey. The Food and Drug Administration is a pussy cat in comparison. Adulterants in the 19th and early 20th centuries were alum and copper sulfate used to improve the baking qualities of inferior flour. Thanks to farm subsidies, the price of flour is so low that adulteration is no longer a serious threat. A good thing too, because it's very difficult to get the ear of a corporation.

In making dough, temperature is important. If the dough is too warm, it will ferment too quickly or become over-fermented. If too cold, the dough will take too long to ferment. Most doughs require a temperature of about 80° F. Temperature is usually controlled by room temperature and the temperature of the water added to the dough. This dough thermometer is intended for the large dough batches of commercial bakeries. Electronic thermometers have superseded this type in most commercial bakeries.

No maker's marks. Dates from early 20th century.

Alcohol thermometer inside glass cylinder reads from 40° to 120° F.

Wooden handle and worn nickel-plated brass. Length: 25 in.

See "Industrial Thermometer" and "Temperature Potentiometer."

Bread bakery at the end of the 19th century.

Here is a half-baked definition of a breadwinner: one who, for the same dough, gets a baker's dozen instead of 12 loaves.

Dough thermometer - same type, quality and period - 2005 - $60

Steelyard

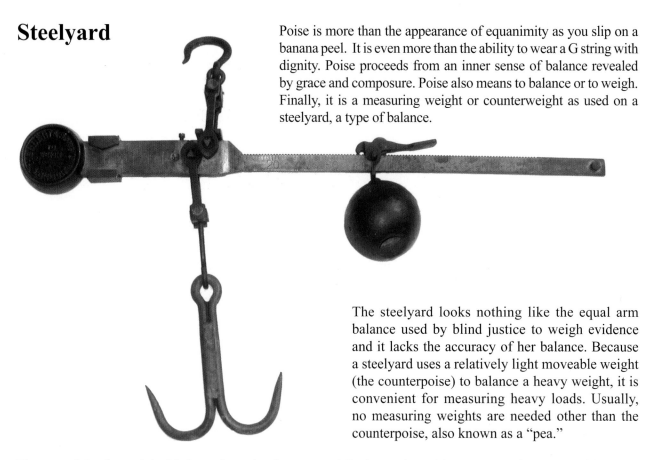

Poise is more than the appearance of equanimity as you slip on a banana peel. It is even more than the ability to wear a G string with dignity. Poise proceeds from an inner sense of balance revealed by grace and composure. Poise also means to balance or to weigh. Finally, it is a measuring weight or counterweight as used on a steelyard, a type of balance.

The steelyard looks nothing like the equal arm balance used by blind justice to weigh evidence and it lacks the accuracy of her balance. Because a steelyard uses a relatively light moveable weight (the counterpoise) to balance a heavy weight, it is convenient for measuring heavy loads. Usually, no measuring weights are needed other than the counterpoise, also known as a "pea."

The material to be weighed is hung from the short arm while the graduated long arm carries a moveable counterpoise. One adjusts the counterpoise until the arms on either side of the fulcrum are in equilibrium and then the weight is read from the graduated arm.

This steelyard can weigh up to 200 pounds. A weighman used it to measure such bulk products as grain, seeds, flour, hides or other commodities *avoirdupois* ("sold by weight" or "to have some peas"). The lever has serrations along the top edge allowing the spherical counterpoise with locking lever to lock in position. On the short side of the lever with the hooks, a sliding brass weight with pointer moves along a short scale to register fractions of a pound. The fulcrum is a triangular-shaped piece of hardened steel or "knife edge." Above the fulcrum, opposing pointers show when the scale balances.

Herbert & Sons, Ltd., London, made this scale. Thomas Herbert was a London scalemaker from 1842. His sons named his firm Herbert & Sons in 1910. The firm survives as The Herbert Group, making electronic scales and labeling devices.

Circular verification stamp on short arm of lever

Overall length: 34 1/4 in.

Long arm scale: 0 to 200 lbs. in one-pound increments

Cast into disk weight on short arm: To Weigh 200 lb.

Short arm scale: 0 to 2 lbs. in 1/4-pound increments

Below is a steelyard you might find in the village market to weigh produce.

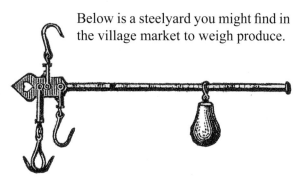

See "Analytical Balance" and "Torsion Balance."

Steelyard - same type, quality and period - 1977 - $50

Watchmaker's Lathe

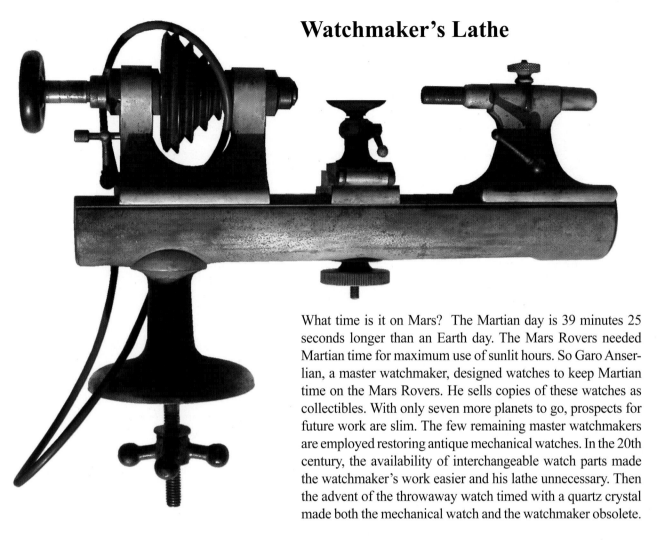

What time is it on Mars? The Martian day is 39 minutes 25 seconds longer than an Earth day. The Mars Rovers needed Martian time for maximum use of sunlit hours. So Garo Anserlian, a master watchmaker, designed watches to keep Martian time on the Mars Rovers. He sells copies of these watches as collectibles. With only seven more planets to go, prospects for future work are slim. The few remaining master watchmakers are employed restoring antique mechanical watches. In the 20th century, the availability of interchangeable watch parts made the watchmaker's work easier and his lathe unnecessary. Then the advent of the throwaway watch timed with a quartz crystal made both the mechanical watch and the watchmaker obsolete.

This is a Webster-Whitcomb type lathe and was the most common watchmaker's lathe in the late 19th and first half of the 20th centuries. The cutting bit or graver is hand-held and placed on the tool rest similar to that of a wood lathe rather than fixed in a compound rest on a carriage as in larger metal-cutting lathes. One of the most delicate parts of a mechanical watch is the pivots on the balance wheel staff. If one of these break, a new staff with pivots can be turned on this lathe.

In the modern watch, we have exchanged rubies for a quartz crystal. Perhaps you can recall the time before the quartz crystal watch when the quality of a watch was designated as 15 jewel, 17 jewel, 19 jewel or 21 jewel. At this late date you are about to learn the meaning of this obscure quality designation. Each wheel (or gear) in a watch is fixed to a staff (an axle). The ends of the staffs rotate in holes which may have jeweled bearings, two to a staff. The balance wheel and lever have a total of nine jewels. These jewels make up the basic suite. A 15-jewel watch would have three more of its staffs with two bearing jewels each (9 plus 6). A 21-jewel watch would have six more of its staffs with two bearing jewels each (9 plus 12). These jewels were rubies.

According to the ancients, rubies conferred protection from poison and the plague, diminished the ill effects of luxury, banished grief and diverted the mind from evil thoughts. Quartz crystals confer accuracy. What's your preference?

Watchmaker's lathe: nickel plated steel
Length: 12 in.

Watchmaker's lathe - same type, quality and period - 2006 - $90

See "Watch."

Glass Cutter

Kohinoor, Cullinan, Tiffany, Hope: the names of the greatest diamonds evoke mystery, romance, beauty and power. Other diamonds, far inferior, serve the mundane purposes of industry. Their name is "bort." Sounds like the grunt of some wild beast.

Diamond is the hardest substance known. It can be cut mechanically only by other diamonds. Its naturally occurring crystalline form is shown to the right. In industry, diamond grit is used to cut and polish diamonds and other hard materials. Bort, as individual industrial diamonds, is used in cutting and drilling tools and to dress or smooth grindstones. Synthetic diamonds are now used along with natural bort for industrial purposes.

Another use of bort is in the glazier's glass cutter as shown here Common contemporary glass cutters use a hardened steel wheel to score the glass for a smooth break or cut. Earlier glass cutters used a small rough diamond for this purpose. The diamond is fixed in a cylindrical brass base and inserted in the cutter, on the right edge of this example. When drawn across the glass at a constant speed, it should make a singing sound. Professional glass cutters with diamond points are in current use.

The National Museum of Iraq in Baghdad contained some of the greatest treasures of human history, artifacts of the earliest civilization in Mesopotamia. During the second Iraq War, through the week of April 8, 2003, the museum was looted. According to Donny George, the museum's director, the loot included tablets containing some of the earliest writing and other antiquities dating as far back as 3,100 BC. At a press conference, Donny George claimed that some of the looting was planned and knowledgeable in that reproductions of artifacts were not stolen. As further proof of planning, he showed the tools used by the looters to open the museum's display cases: diamond-pointed glass cutters.

Stamped into steel fitting:

> PH. SINSZ CO
> BALTIMORE
> PATENT MAY 22 94

A conventional glass cutter with steel scoring wheel

Glass cutter with ebony handle, diamond point and nickel-plated steel fitting. Length: 3 3/4 in.

A very similar glass cutter with an ivory handle made by the same company has a patent date of September 7, 1875.

Glass cutter - same type, quality and period - 1997 - $31

Thread Counter

The white sale for April White of Clermont, Florida, was disappointing. When the 800 thread-count sheets she purchased from Bed Bath & Beyond for $169.99 ripped, she felt ripped off. She took the sheets to a lab that counted about 400 horizontal and vertical threads per square inch in accordance with Federal Trade Commission standards. She was short-sheeted by 400 threads per square inch. April launched a class action suit seeking $5 million in damages for the company's yarn. Bed Bath & Beyond said they counted the number of plies (strands twisted into threads), a count *not* according to Federal Trade Commission standards.

The litigants reached a settlement. Bed Bath & Beyond promised to comply with FTC standards, buyers can return mislabeled sheets for a full refund or keep the sheets and receive a $10 gift certificate or a 20% discount certificate. Meanwhile, April's lawyers received $475,000. You decide who won the case.

The thread counter you see here was too old to figure in this case, very early 20th century. It consists of an adjustable magnifying scope, a thumb-wheel driven pointer and a three-sided rotatable bar with silvered scales. The scales read in inches, millimeters or lines. While looking through the scope, one can move the pointer along the scale as one counts the threads.

This thread counter was manufactured by the Chronik Brothers who also manufactured 35 mm. projectors as early as 1899. The device was distributed by Charles Lowinson of New York. A probable market was the New York garment industry. Latest patent date: 1910. Electronic and digital thread counters have displaced these manual thread counters. The modern versions provide instant counts with great accuracy. Who would use thread counters? Buyers, sellers and weavers of fabrics.

Thread counter: brass. Width: 3 3/8 in. Depth: 2 1/2 in.

Thread counter - same type, quality and period - 2008 - $100

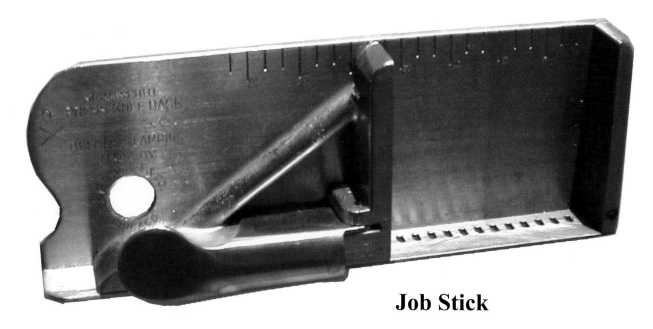

Job Stick

Mark Twain, famed for his brilliant humor and poor investments, lost a fortune on typesetting machines that failed to work. As a 19th-century newspaper reporter and author, Twain knew that printing was labor intensive. Setting type manually required many hours, often longer than the press run itself. Returning type to storage in the California job case also took many hours of work by the printer's devil, a typesetter's apprentice, usually a young boy. The California job case stored type in compartments of a size roughly proportional to the letter's frequency of use. The typesetter or composer held this job stick, a form of type clamp, in his left hand. Reading upside down and backwards, he placed type one letter at a time in the job stick. Then blocks of type from the job stick were locked into a larger frame mounted on the press.

California job case

Unfortunately, the Linotype was too late for Mark Twain's investment portfolio. The Linotype, a line type casting machine, eventually threw most printers, typesetters and printer's devils out of work. Now, the computer has thrown most Linotype operators out of work.

Job sticks come in many lengths, depending on the desired column width. This one is stainless steel and 5 3/4 in. long. It was manufactured by H. B. Rouse & Co. of Chicago, Illinois. This company manufactured printer supplies and now manufactures machine tools.

Job stick - same type, quality and period - 2009 - $65

Buggy Whip

A buggy whip is a fitting conclusion for this collection. It is the metaphor for obsolescence and the low-tech tool of the obsolete coachman. In 1915, the U. S. horse population reached its maximum of about 25 million. Shortly thereafter, the number of horseless carriages exceeded the number of horses. In opposing protectionism, classical economists argued that preserving the market niche for buggy whips would have inhibited growth of the auto industry. Contemporary green economists argue that inhibiting auto production could be a good idea.

In the United States, a buggy was a two-person horse drawn carriage. Amish groups in Pennsylvania and the Midwest still prefer the buggy as a mode of transportation. Buggy rides survive as tourist attractions in New York's Central Park and in other cities. In language, "horse and buggy" survives as a reference to outmoded thinking.

Buggy whips differ from other whips by their long staff and short lash or "popper" at the end. Hand-plaited yarn was used for this whip and then lacquered. Overall length: 65 in.

Buggy whip - same type, quality and period - 2009 - $70

Occupational technology update

Occupations disappear as did the proverbial buggy whip maker. The Economic Research Institute maintains a log of disappearing American jobs. According to their criterion, a job "disappears" when less than 15 persons are so employed. A few of the hundreds of jobs that disappeared from 2001 to 2004 are listed here under the nominal causes of their extinction.

Occupations disappear because:

> A machine performs the task faster, better or cheaper than a human can. Recent examples: bologna lacer, apprentice typesetter, candle cutter, scullion, telegrapher, steam shovel firer, envelope folder, refrigerator car icer, hand cigar bander, hand baseball sewer

> The work product of the occupation is obsolete. Recent examples: sponge diver, record changer assembler, clock winder, linotype machinist apprentice, photoflash powder mixer, watch parts inspector, asbestos siding installer, wolf hunter

> Tastes or fashions changed. Recent examples: human projectile, corset fitter, singing messenger, rabbit dresser, animal impersonator, rattlesnake farmer, sword swallower

There are precedents for massive changes in occupations. American jobs have disappeared because of historical and fundamental shifts in our economy. As agricultural productivity and efficiency increased in the 19th century, surplus farm workers were absorbed by a growing manufacturing sector. As manufacturing productivity and efficiency increased in the 20th century, surplus factory workers were absorbed by a growing service industry. But, as the service industry labor market becomes saturated in the 21st century, where will surplus service industry workers find jobs? It's doubtful if new technologies will absorb the unemployed. How many video game designers do we really need?

10 COLLECTING

Historical Technology as Art
Acquisition
Valuation
Research
Dating Historical Technology
Fakes, Forgeries and Reproductions
Cleaning, Conservation and Restoration
About Technology

John Rezinkoff of Connecticut has collected 115 locks of celebrity hair and was once offered $50,000 for his sample from Abraham Lincoln. Since 1983, Richard Sangster of Holland has collected over 10,000 aluminum beverage cans. Louise J. Greenfarb has collected more than 29,000 fridge magnets. Brian Viner of Great Britain has a collection 3,750 different unused band-aids.

Some anthropologists believe the urge to collect is due to the hunter-gatherer gene gone bonkers. One of the forms of obsessive compulsive personality disorder is collecting. Psychologists have elevated extreme examples to a psychosis. Compulsive collectors may do so because it reduces anxiety. That's the upside. On the downside, pathological collecting interferes with normal relationships and a healthy life style. With this caveat, we are happy to offer the following suggestions for collecting historical technology.

Historical Technology as Art

Rescue a six-foot steam engine connecting rod and crosshead from the junkyard. Clean and polish it and you'll have a stunning stand-alone sculpture. Many old machinery parts show the same functionalism and strength as great dinosaur bones. The goal here is to persuade you to look at objects of early technology as works of beauty and to enjoy them as art.

The shapes, contours and finishes of old technology are as subtle and complex as any contemporary art. You could compare a hanging steelyard balance to a Calder mobile. A Fresnel lens is the essence of the Cubist's art. A ship's propeller has every bit of the sensualism of a flowing Brancussi sculpture. There is an unspoken aesthetic in historical technology that transcends utility. No public relations flak or art impresario trumpeted the artistic merit of these works. Yet, many of them are spectacularly beautiful.

Some of these technological objects are so visually attractive they evoke a sense of wonder. An old Powel & Lealand microscope or a Breguet watch movement may have that effect. The best antique hand tools are so beautifully sculpted that one can easily visualize the craftsman's hands as an essential part of the tool.

Boiler tube cleaner

You can view historical technology as sculpture. These objects have depth and dimensionality, complex planes, compound curving surfaces and changing textures. The wonderful variety of materials, often within the same object, add to their character. A sextant combines wood, brass, steel, silver and glass into a sculpture that was once functional.

The shapes vary between geometrical and organic. And they are not just static sculptures, they are mobiles. Some have intricately choreographed changing relationships between their parts. You have only to watch the moving pendulum and wheels of a skeleton clock, the flying balls of a governor or the revolutions of an orrery.

The shapes, textures and movement of these objects command our attention and appreciation. As collectors, we don't have to go to a museum or art gallery to find them. We can handle the object and get the feel of the thing. That's truly enjoying sculpture.

If you have such an object near you, take a few moments, clear your mind of its technical significance. Take a fresh look. It is art. Enjoy its beauty.

Governor

Hat block

Acquisition

What does it take to spot a treasure of historical technology? Knowledge helps, but curiosity is most important whether you're a novice or an expert. What does this thing do and why did someone make it? How did they make it and why did they use these materials? Finding the answers is rewarding.

These treasures are still out there in flea markets and junkyards, tarnished, covered with dust and unappreciated. Sometimes, the seller has no idea of the object's use or history. These objects frequently cost less now than when they were made. With these opportunities and a little diligence you can acquire beautiful and fascinating historical technology at very reasonable prices.

For the beginning collector, specialization may be the best route. You're much less likely to overpay or purchase items of little interest. A few reference books dealing with your specialty area is the only research investment you'll need. Here are just a few of the common areas of specialization:

Agricultural technology
Astronomical instruments and models
Automobile related items
Cameras and photographic equipment
Calculating devices
Clocks and watches
Drafting tools
Electrical items
Engines of all kinds
Engineering tools and measuring instruments
Guns
Industrial technology
Kitchen equipment
Lighting
Measuring devices

Microscopes
Nautical technology
Navigational instruments
Medical instruments
Radios
Railroad items
Scientific educational and
    demonstration apparatus
Scientific research instruments
    and apparatus
Surveying equipment and
    instruments
Telescopes
Tools
Tractors

If you already have a broad understanding of technology and some knowledge of manufacturing processes, then you are well equipped for the hunt. You are ready to compete with Indiana Jones.

Negotiate. Scrounging is part of the fun. Sure, you'll see acres of Beam bottles, Hummel figurines and similar cooky cutter items made as collectibles. Somewhere, hidden in the rubble, is a beautiful and fascinating item of historical technology. When you find it, don't betray your enthusiasm. If the item is not marked, calmly find out the price. No matter what the price is say, "That's more than I'd expect to pay." Then, negotiate. Never accept the first price offered. At the very least, you can get ten percent off and maybe a good deal more. If you're buying two or more items, you should be able to get a batch discount. Instead of ten bucks each, try fifteen for both.

Sources. Here are some tips for finding them and getting the best deals. Local or community newspapers are a good place to learn about upcoming yard sales, garage sales, rummage sales, flea markets and swap meets. You'll need to get there at opening time to beat out competing antiques dealers and other collectors. Antique tractor and engine associations regularly hold swap meets. Usually, there is a flea market at engine and tractor shows. These are excellent hunting grounds for early technology. And you'll see a lot of interesting old technology even if you don't buy anything.

Junkyard managers (and their dogs) do not permit persons to wander at random through their yards. Still, if you have something specific in mind, you can always ask. Often, junkyard owners will set aside objects they suspect may have collectible value. If you can, get on a friendly basis with the junkyard owner and let him know about your special interests.

Local auctions are fun and sometimes productive. Take advantage of the pre-auction inspection period and examine the objects at your leisure. What you see is what you get with no returns. During this inspection, determine the maximum price you will pay for an item- and then stick to it. Don't get caught up in a bidding war. A down side to auctions is that you may be interested in only one item, but you don't know when that item is going on the block. You can waste a lot of time waiting. Sometimes you can let the auctioneer know of your interest and he'll move up the sale or tell you when the item will go on the block. As to bidding tactics, some prefer to show their commitment by rapid response from the beginning, hoping to intimidate competitors. Others lie low, wait for the bidding to slow down and then step in with the advantage of surprise. Your choice.

The internet is another source of historical technology. You can search for a particular type of object, transits or sewing machines, for example. Several dealers specializing in scientific instruments have web sites. Thousands of antiques dealers, some of whom stock historical technology, have web sites. Browsing these sites gives you pricing information and may be productive for purchases.

Antiques stores and antiques consignment malls are probably the most expensive places to buy historical technology. At consignment malls, a ten percent discount is virtually standard, but you won't get it unless you negotiate. For big ticket items, a hundred dollars or more, negotiating may be even more productive. For the expensive items, the mall manager may agree to call the consignor with your offer. The manager gets his cut regardless of the price and some sale is better than no sale. A final tip: at antiques stores, never trust the sign in the window that says "Open."

The sources for the objects in this book break down approximately as follows:

Flea markets	37 %
Antiques stores	23%
Auctions	17 %
Antiques malls	17 %
Engine swap meets	6 %

Happy hunting.

Valuation

There are certain categories of technology for which there is an established market. Prices within these categories are fairly easy to track. Example categories are microscopes, cameras, radios, telescopes, weapons and so on. Values are much more difficult to determine for items off the beaten path, even though they may be more interesting than items which are conventionally collected.

Comparison pricing. Document your collection. At a minimum, record the item with unambiguous identification, when bought, seller, price paid and estimated value. Initially, the estimated value will be the price paid. As you scrounge through antique stores, flea markets, swap meets, the internet and junkyards, check on prices not only for the things you wish to buy, but also for the things you have already bought. In this way, you will develop a concept of the changing value of your existing collection. As prices change for a particular item, revise estimated value for that item in your collection.

Auction catalogs, price guides and the internet. Sotheby's and Christie's hold occasional auctions of scientific instruments and early technology. The catalogs contain pre-auction estimated prices. If you purchase catalogs for past or upcoming auctions directly from the auction house, you'll receive a listing of actual prices paid. There can be a very wide spread between the pre-auction estimate and the price actually paid. The actual prices paid are probably the most reliable guides to the current market value of very similar items. Antiques price guides such as *Miller's International Antiques Price Guide* are helpful references for objects within established categories. Browsing the internet for historical technology is fun and informative. You learn what others are collecting and how they value it. Search engines help you find specific categories of items at antiques dealers and at on-line auction houses.

Appraisals. Appraisals may be suspect. The motive for the appraisal can affect the appraiser's valuation: higher valuation for insurance or resale, lower valuation for estates. The appraisal fee should be fixed, based on the appraiser's time and not a percentage of the total appraised value. Appraisal fees based on percentage of value tend to inflate valuation. Appraisal of objects of historical technology is difficult and beyond the knowledge of most antiques dealers. The same condition that made an object a bargain in the first place, the dealer's ignorance of the nature or use of the object, can make that object difficult to value. If you're getting an appraisal, be sure to find a specialist, someone specifically experienced and knowledgeable in valuing historical technology.

Factors affecting value. These are rarity, condition, materials and workmanship, technological and historical significance and appreciation through increasing demand. Rarity is an important pricing factor for objects within established collectable categories where there is collector competition. Rare objects outside such categories tend to have highly variable prices and other factors have a stronger influence on price.

To evaluate condition, consider the object's completeness, absence of breakage, repair or replacement and original finish. Signs of normal usage and wear may actually enhance an objects value by demonstrating its authenticity. By the same token, restoration through painting, re-lacquering or re-blueing can lower value. The older an object, the greater is the price toleration for poor condition.

Materials and workmanship affect value. Materials with higher intrinsic value add to the price, as does labor-intensive manufacture versus cheaper methods. Compare a microscope made of brass with one of sheet steel from the same period. You'll find that more expensive machining methods were used on the brass microscope. Makers tend *not* to use expensive methods to work cheap materials or cheap methods to work expensive materials. With few exceptions quality, or lack of it, will be evident and consistent for both materials and workmanship in the same item.

Some objects have great significance in the history of technology and this fact enhances their value. An example is scientific equipment used in a pioneering experiment or apparatus known to have belonged to a noted scientist. Scientific instruments carrying the names of noted innovators or makers have greater value. Objects using a newly introduced technology, whether successful or not, have greater value. Experimental models and patent models are highly collectable and valuable. Usually, objects with a very low serial number have greater value than later examples of the same object.

Interest in historical technology and the collection of historical technology is growing. This is evidenced by increasing market prices and the numbers of shows and auctions featuring early technology. As demand increases for these items, so will the value of existing collections. Appreciation will be monetary as well as aesthetic.

For many of the items in this book, you will find market price by year at the bottom of the page. These prices were taken from auction catalogs, dealer catalogs and price guides showing very similar items. For some objects, appraisal values were used. Note that the price trend is not always upwards. A few items of historical technology have dropped in value, though most continue to rise in value.

Research

Carl Sagan said that, "We live in a society exquisitely dependent on science and technology, in which hardly anyone knows anything about science and technology." Researching historical technology makes you the exception.

Part of the joy of collecting is learning how things work. Historical technology provokes questions. What is it? What does it do? How does it work? Who made it? How was it made? Once you identify function as specifically as possible, answers to the other questions are a lot easier. Initially, you'll need patience and persistence. In many situations, photographs of the object in question will be useful. When seeking information from individuals or experts, have your questions prepared beforehand so you can use their time to best advantage. We'll take a look at research resources.

Library. The bigger the better. Larger libraries have computerized catalog files. You can access the collection by subject. Descriptive classifications are arbitrary. If you were researching a Stirling cycle engine, you may have to look up "Stirling cycle", "Ericsson engine", "hot air engine", "air engine" and "engine." You can use general references first, such as encyclopedias, to narrow the scope of your search. The Dewey decimal code for pure science is 500 through 599 and 600 through 699 for technology. Librarians are very helpful. Don't hesitate to ask. Most librarians will pick up a research question as a challenge. You are most likely to get their help if you are at the library during weekdays. Some libraries have collections of trade periodicals. If you can find a relevant trade publication and it doesn't contain the information you want, you may phone a publication staff member with your questions.

Other collectors and dealers. You know who they are. Often, other collectors and dealers are flattered by your inquiry. Expect to find a generous and helpful response. Trading information with others who share your enthusiasm is a pleasure. If you can't get information directly on point, you'll get suggestions for other resources to consult.

Special interest societies, trade and industrial associations, professional societies. Some libraries have directories of associations and there are thousands of associations. You may be able to find an association concerned with some aspect of the object you are researching. The *Encyclopedia of Associations* published by Gale Research can guide you to groups such as the Antique Scale Collectors Association and the Antique Telephone Collectors Association. The association phone numbers and addresses are in the Encyclopedia. You can call to find someone with expertise in your research subject.

Internet. You can use one of the search engines on the internet to gather information. You can search by the name of the object, by the maker's name or by the trade, profession or discipline related to the object. Some useful references are likely to turn up among the hundreds of unrelated references the search engine will produce. On the net, Amazon.com and Alibris.com have huge listings of books accessed by subject. Some of these could be useful.

Chambers of Commerce and historical societies. If you can locate the town where an object was made, the Chamber of Commerce, local historical society or local museum may be able to give you more information based on the maker's name. In small to medium-sized towns, these organizations take pride in the history of local manufacturers and are generous with time and information. This approach is less useful for large cities.

Museums. The curators of museum collections related to your area of research may or may not be cooperative, depending on demands for their time. Interviews may not be granted. Be prepared to send photos and a letter with specific questions. Your local library may have a copy of *The Official Museum Directory* published by National Register Publishing. This lists museums by region and by the type of collection. It may be useful in finding a museum with a collection in your area of interest.

Universities. You should identify the relevant academic discipline as specifically as possible. Fielding questions from the public is not a responsibility of faculty. However, they may choose to respond for the public relations benefit. Do your homework first before using this resource. Faculty members may regard obvious or simple questions as a waste of their time. Interviews may not be granted, so prepare to send photos and a letter with specific questions.

Dating Historical Technology

How do you find the approximate date of an item of historical technology? Here are suggestions to minimize research effort and false leads.

The obvious. Plaques and the item itself may carry patent dates and patent numbers. The latest patent date gives you a reasonable beginning date for the age of the object. Patent numbers by year are shown in an accompanying table. For engineering, navigational and scientific instruments, the cases often contain dated inspection and calibration certificates. Accompanying manuals may be dated by copyright. Trade cards included in cases may have a date or provide some leads to dating.

Researching the maker's name can establish dates. Bear in mind that, for 19th-century objects, the distributor's name rather than the maker's name may be found on the object. For items of historical technology that are regularly collected, auction catalogs and reference books (see the Bibliography) are helpful in dating.

Let's consider some arbitrary definitions applied to items of historical technology. We'll move from the general to the increasingly specific and transient: function, mechanism and design. The watch serves as an example.

Function is the purpose for which the item was made, what it does, its *raison d'etre.* The function of a watch is easily portable timekeeping. This basic function remains unchanged from the 16th century where the balance is controlled by a hog's bristle to a contemporary quartz crystal digital LED watch. Function becomes obsolescent if it is directly related to obsolescent mechanisms. A balance wheel poising tool lost its function with the obsolescence of the balance wheel. The steam engine indicator became obsolescent with the reciprocating steam engine. Function provides the broadest time bracket for dating.

Mechanism is the specific means by which the item's function is achieved. The mechanism has changed dramatically in the history of the watch. Many types of escapements were developed: verge (16th -17th century), cylinder and detent (18th century), lever (19th century), vibrating fork and quartz crystal (20th century). The escapement itself dates the watch. The power source has moved from key-wound, self-winding, battery to silicon panel. This, too, dates the watch. Technological changes in mechanism are especially useful in dating.

Design is the form, structure and finish of an item apart from that dictated by function and mechanism. True, there are 16th century watches in the shape of a skull and there are 20th century watches in the shape of a skull. But the design, the images and types of ornament can still help us date the watch: religious and mythological references in the 17th century, rural scenes and floral baroque designs in the 18th century, railroad references in the 19th century, throwaway watches to match your ensemble in the 20th century. Design based on contemporary tastes and fashion is likely to change even though function and mechanism do not.

For any item of technology function, mechanism and design may change through time. So, any one of these qualities may be used for dating within specific periods. To minimize the dating effort, it is probably a good idea to date the object from function to mechanism and then design. Finally, look at the manufacturing methods and materials.

Manufacturing methods and materials. If you know something of machining processes and when different manufacturing methods and materials were introduced, you have another handle on dating. Machining processes leave distinctive marks if they are not polished away. Examples are circumferential lines for lathe turning and spinning, die gouges for sheet metal stamping, sprue hole traces and mold marks for casting, and parallel or circular scrapes for milling. For a truly problematic item, recognizing the manufacturing process marks and knowing when those processes were first used can help dating.

Different materials require different machining processes: spinning for sheet metal, milling or turning for castings, forging for high-strength parts and so on. The combination of dated machining process and dated introduction of materials can further narrow the date bracket for an item. These dates of invention or introduction may surprise you as earlier than expected. They may help you date some object.

Dates of Invention or Introduction for Materials, Processes, Devices and Fasteners

Materials

Rubber	1800
Tin plate	1820
Celluloid	1870
Aluminum	1887
Bakelite	1909
Stainless steel	1911
Polyvinyl chloride	1927
Plexiglas	1935

Processes

Sheffield plate, laminating thin silver sheet to copper	1742
Electroplating	1840
Industrial galvanizing	1840
Metal machining by milling	1862
Metal machining by planing	1862
Carbon arc welding	1885
Manufacture of seamless tubing	1885
Oxyacetylene welding	1903

Devices and Fasteners

Ball bearings	1794
Whitworth screw thread standardized	1860
Stapler	1868
Phillips head screw	1930

Table of Issue Years and Patent Numbers for U.S. Patents Issued Since 1836

Issue Year	Highest Number	Issue Year	Highest Number	Issue Year	Highest Number	Issue Year	Highest Number
1836	0000001	1877	0185813	1918	1251458	1959	2866973
1837	0000110	1878	0198733	1919	1290027	1960	2919443
1838	0000546	1879	0211078	1920	1326899	1961	2966681
1839	0001061	1880	0223211	1921	1364063	1962	3015103
1840	0001465	1881	0236137	1922	1401948	1963	3070801
1841	0001923	1882	0251685	1923	1440362	1964	3116487
1842	0002413	1883	0269820	1924	1478996	1965	3163865
1843	0002901	1884	0291016	1925	1521590	1966	3226729
1844	0003395	1885	0310163	1926	1568040	1967	3295143
1845	0003873	1886	0333494	1927	1612700	1968	3360800
1846	0004348	1887	0355291	1928	1654521	1969	3419907
1847	0004914	1888	0375720	1929	1696897	1970	3487470
1848	0005409	1889	0395305	1930	1742181	1971	3551909
1849	0005993	1890	0418665	1931	1787424	1972	3631539
1850	0006981	1891	0443987	1932	1839190	1973	3707729
1851	0007865	1892	0466315	1933	1892663	1974	3781914
1852	0008622	1893	0488976	1934	1941449	1975	3858241
1853	0009512	1894	0511744	1935	1985878	1976	3930271
1854	0010358	1895	0531619	1936	2026516	1977	4000520
1855	0012117	1896	0552502	1937	2066309	1978	4065812
1856	0014009	1897	0574369	1938	2104004	1979	4131952
1857	0016324	1898	0596467	1939	2142080	1980	4180867
1858	0019010	1899	0616871	1940	2185170	1981	4242757
1859	0022477	1900	0640167	1941	2227418	1982	4308622
1860	0026642	1901	0664827	1942	2268540	1983	4366579
1861	0031005	1902	0690385	1943	2307007	1984	4423523
1862	0034045	1903	0717521	1944	2338081	1985	4490855
1863	0037266	1904	0748567	1945	2366154	1986	4562596
1864	0041047	1905	0778834	1946	2391856	1987	4633526
1865	0045685	1906	0808618	1947	2413675	1988	4716594
1866	0051784	1907	0839799	1948	2433824	1989	4794652
1867	0060658	1908	0875679	1949	2457797	1990	4890335
1868	0072959	1909	0908436	1950	2492944	1991	4980927
1869	0085503	1910	0945010	1951	2536016	1992	5077836
1870	0098460	1911	0980178	1952	2580379	1993	5175886
1871	0110617	1912	1013095	1953	2624046	1994	5274846
1872	0122304	1913	1049326	1954	2664562	1995	5377359
1873	0134504	1914	1083267	1955	2698434	1996	5479658
1874	0146120	1915	1123212	1956	2728913	1997	5590420
1875	0158350	1916	1166419	1957	2775762	1998	5704062
1876	0171641	1917	1210389	1958	2818567	1999	5855021

Fakes, Forgeries and Reproductions

You'd be correct in assuming that the 17th-century astrolabe you saw in an antique store for $150 was a fake. That's easy. A cheap knock-off for decorating purposes is not the problem. Now, less well known 19th-century and early 20th-century items of technology are being manufactured as reproductions — or fakes. Here are a few examples:

Balance scales of all periods	Microscopes of the 18th century
Binnacles	Octants
Box sextants	Pocket sextants
Clinometers	Reflecting telescopes
Clocks	Sextants
Fowler phrenological busts	Ship's lights and lanterns
Mark V navy diving helmets	Sun dials
Miner's safety lamps	Weapons
	Whaling tools

Antique scientific instruments are being reproduced in India and Hong Kong. In some cases, excellent workmanship is invested in these reproductions. Manufacturing methods and materials may faithfully copy the original. Often, however, a detail is overlooked. In the case of the diving helmet, faults in the breastplate and a missing internal chin-operated air valve betray the fake. How can you protect yourself from these fakes or honest reproductions sold as authentic?

Price. Unrealistic pricing is a good clue. If it's a real steal, there's a probability that you're the one being stolen from. Knowledge of prices earned through comparison pricing and auction catalogs suggest whether a very low price should arouse suspicion and provoke an extra close examination of the object or the circumstances of the sale. A very low price for an obscure piece of technology is reasonable. A very low price for a damaged or broken piece of technology is reasonable. A very low price for a well-made, popular piece of technology in good condition is unreasonable and makes the piece suspect.

Condition. Does the object look new? Is the condition too good? Does the item show signs of use and wear at appropriate points? Although tarnish and patina can be faked, these should be present where appropriate — and absent at points of wear if the object has been recently used. Damage, breakage or missing parts may be an indicator of authenticity; so can evident repairs and replacement parts. The greater the putative age of an object, the poorer the condition is likely to be. A one hundred-year old object in pristine condition is highly suspect.

Source. Where did the seller get the object? There's no harm in asking. Is the answer reasonable considering the type of object? If there's hesitation or evasiveness in the reply, that suggests caution. Does the seller represent the object as authentic? Will he or she guarantee authenticity? Once again, there's no harm in asking. Often, reproductions are sold in an area where the original was manufactured. Local museums sometimes produce and sell reproductions. Could there be such a local source for reproductions on the local market?

Makers' marks. Look for makers' marks. They should be complete, correct and in the appropriate style. If the plaque says "Navy Sextant" instead of "U.S. Navy Sextant", you know it's a reproduction. Often, the type font used in the maker's mark is incorrect in the reproduction. The more daring forgers will reproduce the makers' marks, including names, logos and patent numbers and plaques in their entirety. It still helps to be alert for qualifications and caveats buried in the makers' marks suggesting a reproduction. Phrases such as *"in the style of Ross"* or a *"Ross-type"* may be code language for reproduction. Misspelling a prominent maker's name is an escape clause for the forger.

Manufacturing methods and materials. Knowledge of manufacturing processes, their relevance to shapes and materials and the marks left by those processes is extremely valuable. Anachronisms are evident when the process does not match the historic period. Manufacturing process marks should be appropriate, bearing in mind that these marks may have been polished or worn away. Very sharp machined edges and burrs betray recent manufacture.

Are calibration marks or numbers stamped or engraved? Calibration marks on older and high-quality instruments are engraved. If such marks are stamped, the instrument is of recent manufacture or a reproduction.

For castings, are mold marks and sprue hole traces where you would expect to find them? Is the surface texture right for a casting? Of course, castings may be subsequently machined. In reproductions, castings are often substituted for parts that were originally machined.

Where items should have been turned, are there lathe tool marks?

Where surfaces should have been milled, are the tool markings appropriate?

For forgings, are hammer or other tool marks present?

For joints, are welded, brazed or soldered joints where they should be considering the type and age of the object?

Where sheet metal items should be hand planished, is there evidence that the object was spun?

For sheet metal, are stampings used where another process would originally have been used?

Are parts bent where they would have originally been cast or machined?

Fasteners and accessory hardware may reveal reproduction when they are inconsistent with other features of the object.

Are fasteners appropriate for the period and type of object: rivets, screws, bolts, nails, tacks, clips and so on? Phillips head screws in a 19th-century item are a dead giveaway.

Nails and spikes can be dated according to the type of head.

In a detailed study of an object, the type of screw thread used may be a clue to authenticity? Is the authentic thread American National Standard, metric or British Standard?

The surface finish: paint, plating, polishing and engine turning are indicators of authenticity. Tastes and fashions in paint colors, even for items of technology, change with the times. For example, olive paint was popular for mechanical and electrical items from about 1910 to 1930. There are traditions in painting parts of machinery. In the same machine, moving parts may be painted red while structural components are dark green. Castings are usually painted while machined surfaces are left bare.

Nickel-plating of polished castings and small parts was common, and to a much lesser extent, copper plating in the 19th century. Both yielded to chrome plating and brass plating. From the 18th- to the mid-19th centuries, instruments were polished and lacquered. A lacquered brass instrument showing no tarnished scratches or tarnish spotting suggests that the instrument has been refinished or could be a reproduction. Lacquering brass was gradually succeeded by oxidizing which darkened the surface and resisted corrosion. Engine turning is the spiraling or shimmering ornamental finish one finds on the back plate of watches and in some instruments. It may be taken as a sign of quality. If missing or poorly executed, engine turning signals a reproduction. Crudely executed and unworn knurling on thumbwheels signals a reproduction, as well. Familiarity with finishes and their appropriate use helps one distinguish the real from the fake.

In reproductions, brass anodized aluminum or brass-plated iron may substitute for solid brass. A magnet will tell you if your dealing with brass-plated iron. Aluminum will be noticeably light in weight. The patina of old tarnished bronze and brass can be convincingly faked. One clue is a realistic patina on some parts while other parts are bright. Hard rubber (vulcanite, ebonite) was used as early as the 1840s. On instruments, it was used to make knobs, thumbwheels and pushplates. As it ages, it can pick up a brownish matt patina. It can be copied in plastic. The inappropriate use of materials often betrays a fake for what it is.

Familiarity with the type of object. The single best protection against reproductions is a thorough knowledge of the type of object being collected. Often, reproductions are made without a true understanding of the purpose and function of the object. The result is structural or mechanical anomalies that are obvious to students of a particular technology. Indeed, some reproductions are so weird, they may rank as collector's items in a class of their own.

A good question to ask is "Could I actually use this item or would it really work?" If you have sufficient knowledge, the item is complete and undamaged, and it won't do what it's supposed to do, then it could be a clumsy knock-off. Finding out why it won't work reveals the reproduction fault.

For fakes, forgeries and reproductions, a healthy skepticism is your best defense, even if it takes some joy out of the hunt.

Cleaning, Conservation and Restoration

Cleaning. A few conservators argue that the dirt on an object is also a record of its history. To clean the object is to destroy part of its history. Perhaps that view is a bit extreme. Generally, soap and water are a good start. They're also a good end. Think carefully before you escalate the cleaning effort. Distillate solvents and abrasives may do some real damage. Lacquered brass and wood finishes are easily damaged by abrasives and solvents. Always test clean a small, unobtrusive area first.

When disassembling a complicated object for cleaning, it's a good idea to photographically document the object before and during disassembly. You may need these photos for guidance in reassembly. They also provide a before-and-after comparison of your cleaning effort.

A set of fine watchmaker's screw drivers is a necessity for work on instruments. If you're right-handed, use your left hand to keep the driver blade centered and avoid marring screw heads and adjacent areas. During cleaning, keep related small parts in plastic baggies. Cotton swabs are useful, especially for cleaning threaded holes. Cross-threading is a real possibility where very fine threads are used on large circumferences, such as lens bezels. Use special care to prevent cross-threading during reassembly.

Parts of an object that are paper, cardboard, wood, leather or fabric require special protection during cleaning. If possible, fragile or absorbent materials should be separated from the object before liquid cleaning compounds are used. Some brass polishes will corrode adjacent silver. Sometimes masking tape provides sufficient protection. As you would with a repair, think through the entire cleaning process before you start, anticipate and solve possible problems. When in doubt, consult someone with experience.

Conservation. Conservation is preserving an object with as little change as possible. The goal is to prevent further damage or deterioration and freeze the object in time. Continuing deterioration may be due to exposure to the atmosphere producing rust, tarnish or other corrosion; insect attack to parts such as wood, leather, cloth or cardboard; light damage to painted or finished surfaces. Some materials are victims of "inherent vice:" not original sin, but self-destruction due to the nature of the materials used in the object. Examples are the corrosive effect of certain dyes or the gradual embrittlement of rubber parts.

For extremely valuable or historically significant objects, the loss of any material due to restoration is unacceptable. In such cases, conservation is required and only those steps are taken that are necessary to prevent further deterioration.

Restoration. Whether to restore is a very tough question. There is a growing trend to leave it as it is. Yet, restoration by museums and art galleries is a continuing practice. Not only does the public, in general, want to see how things originally looked, but many connoisseurs and collectors have the same desire.

Disadvantages:

For many items, signs of restoration will diminish the monetary value of the object.

Poorly-executed restoration diminishes both monetary and aesthetic value of the object.

After restoration, the object may have a harsh, new appearance, out of character with its true age.

Restoration by experts is labor intensive and costly. There is possible loss of historically significant features.

Advantages:

Tasteful restoration may improve both aesthetic value and monetary value of the object.

The object is usually protected against further deterioration.

Original parts and necessary skills may still be available while this may not be the case in the future.

Since museums regularly restore items of early technology for display, does that give you license to restore? That depends on whether you have the requisite skills, knowledge and judgment. If not, and you are unwilling to pay an expert, leave the object alone and content yourself with cleaning.

Judgment is important. Take the case of the ubiquitous "mad buffer." If you have been collecting for awhile, you've seen his work. He has the skill needed to disassemble and reassemble a microscope. He also has the outrageously bad judgment to polish all the parts on a buffing wheel and destroy original finishes, patina and sharp machined edges.

Thorough research is the first step before any restoration. You will want to match original finishes, materials and manufacturing methods so far as possible. Review reference books. Try to find the same item in a museum, personal collection or show. If possible, photograph it. Note original structures, materials, colors and finishes. Use this information to guide your restoration.

Check on the maker. If the manufacturer is still in business, maybe parts are available. Other collectors, dealers or repair firms may be a source of parts. Determine before any restoration whether you want the object to look new or used. If used, how old should it look? Paints and patinas can be adjusted to give an impression of age.

Maybe you heard the story of George Washington's hatchet, the one he used to chop down his father's cherry tree. The current owner explains that, because of severe rust and a crack in the steel, the head was replaced. Wood worms destroyed the handle, so a new and exact copy of the handle was fitted to the head. The owner insists it is still George Washington's hatchet. You decide how much restoration an antique can sustain and still be authentic, that point when restoration becomes reproduction.

Reused artifacts. At certain points in time, the market is flooded with objects displaced by a new technology: vacuum-tube radios, mechanical watches, slide rules, mechanical adding machines and drafting sets. These technologically obsolete items are so cheap for awhile that almost any alternative use seems reasonable. Eventually, such items may rise in value to the point they are appreciated for what they are and merit rescue from reuse through conservation or restoration.

Items of historical technology may be recycled as decorator items. This may be termed "adaptive use." Examples: lamp bases made of old telephones, electric meters, old tools or almost anything, chairs made of old spinning wheels, fire tools made of old bayonets, lamp shades made of old maps and so on. Some collectors of historical technology may consider this practice as desecration. For many others, it is merely bad taste or kitsch.

About Technology

Let's shift our focus from collecting technology to technology itself. For our purposes, technology is the means of controlling and adapting to our environment. These means include tools, machines, power sources, materials, processes and systems. More skeptically, Max Frisch said, "Technology is arranging the world so we need not experience it."

What is the difference between technology, science and engineering? Technology, beginning with bone and stone tools, predates science and engineering by tens of thousands of years. Science, the rational and verifiable explanation and description of natural phenomena, requires written language and developed only as societies could afford specialization. Engineering is the deliberate design of machines, materials and systems to achieve highly specific goals and may or may not employ scientific knowledge for practical ends.

The frontiers are fuzzy between technology, engineering and science; they may blend one into the other. They have mutual influences. For example, science explains the properties of certain materials. Applying this knowledge, engineers design transistors. Then, transistors are used both in practical communications technology and in scientific research technology. Curiously, what we think of as science fiction is actually technology fiction in that it describes futuristic technology instead of scientific knowledge.

Before written language, technology was transmitted through the relocation and mentoring of craftsmen or by the distribution of their products through trade or conquest. Writing and printing fostered the preservation of technological information as a valuable social and economic asset. Documented technology became the foundation for academic transmission of technology through science and engineering.

The inventive personality. We revere inventors. They are our heros. What are their personality traits? One study found that a third of independent inventors continued to spend money and fifty percent continued to spend time on their projects after receiving authoritative advice to quit. So, confidence, perseverance and optimism are personality traits of inventors. Other studies suggest a need for independence, a desire for challenges and less focus on financial gains than one might expect (sounds like Lorenzo Jones and his devoted wife, Belle). What determines the specific forms of the creative contributions of inventive personalities?

Simultaneous invention. Although individual creative genius is important, the high frequency of simultaneous invention suggests that social and economic needs along with pre-existing technology are the main impetus for specific technological innovations. Restated, social and economic need with enabling technology make some inventions inevitable. Surprise! Necessity really is the mother of invention. Here are a few examples of simultaneous invention:

Octant. About 1730, John Hadley of London and Thomas Godfrey of Philadelphia independently invented the octant, a precursor to the sextant.

Steel manufacturer. In the middle of the 19th Century, the American William Kelly and the Englishman Henry Bessemer independently developed the process of forcing air through molten iron to burn off impurities to make steel.

Telephone. On the same day, February 14, 1876, Alexander Grahm Bell and Elisha Gray independently filed for patents for the telephone at the U.S. Patent Office in Washington, D.C.

Incandescent light bulb. In 1878, the British inventor Joseph Swan invented a carbonized filament derived from paper in a glass bulb at about the same time that Thomas Edison invented a carbonized filament derived from a cotton thread in a glass bulb.

Television. Philo Farnsworth, an American scientist, and a Russian immigrant scientist, Vladimir Zworykin, simultaneously and independently developed television cameras in the late 1920s.

Such coincidental inventions are a feast for patent attorneys.

Accidental discoveries. Accidental discoveries are also a source of technological invention. Of course, recognizing the potential of a lucky accident and converting it into a practical invention may require considerable dedication or genius. Serendipitous events are almost commonplace in the history of technology. Some examples:

X-ray tube. Wilhelm Röntgen discovered X-rays through the accidental exposure of photographic plates to the emissions of a cathode-ray tube in 1895. He developed X-ray tubes as a result. He generously placed his invention in the public domain.

Penicillin. In 1928, Alexander Fleming, a Scottish bacteriologist noted that a staphylococcus strain did not grow in a contaminated area of a culture. The contaminant was a penicillium mold. Through further investigation, he developed the antibiotic, penicillin.

Teflon. Roy J. Plunkett was investigating refrigerants when he found a slippery white substance in a cylinder that should have held refrigerant gas. Instead of discarding the substance, he theorized that the gas had polymerized, producing the substance. In 1938, he discovered the inert properties of the substance, later known as teflon.

Convergent technology. In technological convergence, different technologies combine to produce a new technology. Examples are the manufacture of interchangeable parts combined with the assembly line to create mass production or servo-mechanisms and computers combined in robotics.

Emerging technologies. These technologies potentially displace existing technologies or functions. You could view these as growth opportunities or threats. Biotechnology could displace evolution in the creation of new species. Artificial intelligence could displace human thought processes in research, government, business or industry. Nanomaterials could displace conventional manufacturing materials through their greater strength or versatility.

International expositions of technology. The 19th Century saw the introduction of international expositions. They were opportunities for nationalistic show-and-tell and exercises in bragging rights for new technology. They showcased national engineering and industrial achievements. Usually, there were specific exhibition halls or buildings devoted to machinery, industrial arts, transportation and, finally, electricity. Some expositions:

Crystal Palace

1851 Great Exhibition London. Prince Albert and Queen Victoria promoted this international exposition. Its most prominent feature, the Crystal Palace, housed the exhibition. The Crystal Palace, made of metal rods and glass, covered an area of 990,000 square feet. The building's design was revolutionary. American exhibitions included Colt's repeating pistol, Goodyear's rubber products and McCormick's reaper. Products of English industry included steam engines, hydraulic presses, and spinning machines.

1853 New York Exposition. Elisha Otis first demonstrated his "safety elevator" at this exposition. He had the hoisting rope cut with himself in the cab as it fell and then locked safely in place above the heads of the gasping viewers.

Eiffel Tower

1889 International Exposition Paris. This exposition celebrated the centenary of the French Revolution. Its landmark was Gustave Eiffel's tower, the first major wrought iron structure and, standing 984 feet high, the World's tallest structure until the Chrysler Building of 1930.

1893 Columbian Exposition Chicago. The Columbian Exposition commemorated the 400th anniversary of the discovery of America by Christopher Columbus. For the first time, electricity illuminated an American exposition. George Westinghouse and Nikola Tesla used the event to introduce alternating current. The Exposition also introduced the Ferris Wheel as a technological marvel. Its diameter was 250 feet.

Ferris Wheel

1904 St. Louis Worlds Fair Louisiana Purchase Exposition. One of the major industrial attractions of this exposition was an Allis-Chalmers 5,000-horsepower steam engine standing 40 feet high with a 25-foot flywheel.

These expositions were exuberant celebrations of technology. During the 19th Century, Western society regarded the progress of technology as an unqualified good. Few dissented. Technology brought increasing agricultural and industrial production, improved communications, improved public health and rising standards of living. The common view held that technology could solve most of societies problems. Technology promised Utopia.

The disillusion of the First World War tarnished hopes of a technological Utopia. By the end of the Second World War and the advent of nuclear weapons, a more pessimistic view of technology prevailed. In the 21st Century, we share a growing alarm at the technological by-products of environmental degradation and global warming. Some sociologists observed that we exist in a technological community rather than a human community. As individuals, we are personally isolated from others by technology and this alienation erodes our sense of social responsibility.

Technological benefits have become the fruits of a Faustian bargain and placed us in a dangerous dilemma. Solutions to our dilemma are well within our technological reach. All we need is the will to grasp them.

Antique Technology Collectors Associations

This listing enables you to contact like-minded individuals by means of the internet. These internet sites were accessible as of February 2011.

apple parers *International Society of Apple Parer Enthusiasts* appleparermuseum.com/ISAPEInformation.htm
automobiles *Antique Automobile Club of America* aaca.org
aviation *Antique Airplane Association* antiqueairfield.com
barbed wire *Antique Barbed Wire Society* antiquebarbedwiresociety.com
boats *International Symposium on Boat and Ship Archeology* isbsa.org
cameras *The Chicago Photographic Collectors Society* chicagophotographic.org
clocks and watches *National Association of Watch and Clock Collectors* nawcc.org
engines *Antique Small Engine Collectors Club* asecc.com
fans, mechanical *Antique Fan Collectors Association* fancollectors.org
firearms *The Ohio Gun Collectors Association* ogca.com
firefighting artifacts *Gibson Road Antique Fire Association* grafa.org
fountain pens *Baltimore Fountain Pen Society* baltpens.org
hand tools *Midwest Tool Collectors Association* mwtca.org
industrial archaeology *The Association of Industrial Archaeology* industrial-archaeology.org
lighting *Rushlight Club* rushlight.org
locks *American Lock Collectors Association* alcalocks.com
music boxes *Automatic Musical Instrument Collectors Association* amica.org
outboard motors *The Antique Outboard Motor Club, Inc.* aomci.org
phonographs and gramophones *The City of London Phonograph and Gramophone Society* clpgs.org.uk
projectors *The Magic Lantern Society* magiclantern.org.uk
railroad artifacts *Railrodiana Collectors Association* railroadcollectors.org
radios *Antique Wireless Association* antiquewireless.org
sad irons *Pressing Iron and Trivet Collectors of America* pressingironandtrivetcollectors.org
scales and balances *The International Society of Scale Collectors* isasc.org
scientific instruments *Scientific Instrument Society* sis.org.uk
sewing machines *International Sewing Machine Collectors Society* ismacs.net
slide rules *The Oughtred Society* oughtred.org
steam engines *International Stationary Steam Engine Society* isses.org
stereoscopes *National Stereoscope Association* stereoview.org
stoves and refrigerators *The Old Appliance Club* antiquestoves.com
telephones *Antique Telephone Collectors Association* atcaonline.com
telescopes *The Antique Telescope Society* webari.com/oldscope
toasters *Toaster Collectors Association* toastercollectors.org
tractors *The Early Day Gas Engine and Tractor Association* edgeta.com
trades, crafts, and tools *Early American Industries Association* eaiainfo.org
trucks *American Truck Historical Society* aths.org
typewriters *Early Typewriter Collectors Association* typewriter.rydia.net

Glossary

ampere. A measure of electrical current. The steady current produced by one volt across a resistance of one ohm.

annealing. To heat and cool metal or other substances to render them less brittle and more malleable.

azimuth. The horizontal angle measured between two points clockwise. For a celestial object, it is measured from the object's arc of intersection with the horizon to some terrestrial point along the horizon, or magnetic north.

bearing (navigation). The horizontal direction of one terrestrial point from another. It is usually measured clockwise.

cam. A cam is a turning or sliding piece whose shape imparts a variable or intermittent motion to some other moving part.

collimation. Producing parallel rays of light.

focal length. The distance between the optical center of a lens, or the surface of a mirror, and its focus.

horizon glass. The glass of a marine sextant through which the horizon is observed. This glass is usually half silvered.

horsepower. A measure of work. Five hundred fifty foot-pounds of work per second.

latitude. Angular distance measured and labeled north or south of the equator to 90°.

longitude. Angular distance measured and labeled east or west of the prime meridian (passing through Greenwich, the prime meridian) to 180°.

milling. Shaping metal by means of rotating cutters on a milling machine.

objective. The lens in an optical instrument closest to the object being viewed.

ocular. The lens in an optical instrument closest to the eye.

ohm. A measure of electrical resistance. The resistance of an electrical circuit in which one watt of power is dissipated when one ampere flows through it.

planishing. Shaping sheet metal by hammering it over a form.

polymerization. A chemical reaction in which small molecules combine to form larger, repeating molecular structures.

refraction. The bending of light due to its passage through a transparent or translucent medium. This function is performed by a lens.

solenoid. A coil of wire containing an iron or steel piece that moves when current is applied to the coil.

spinning (metal). Shaping sheet metal by pressing it against a form while it is rapidly spinning. Used primarily for concave shapes.

spline. A thin piece of wood or metal fitting into a grove to hold parts together.

sprue hole The hole in a casting mold into which molten metal is poured.

station (in surveying). A marked point over which an instrument is or will be accurately positioned for use.

traverse line. A line on which a surveying instrument is located.

trunnion. Opposing projecting pins or pivots, such as those on a cannon, serving as an axis about which an object can be turned.

turning. Shaping metal by mounting the workpiece on a lathe where it is rotated against a cutting bit.

vernier. Opposing moveable scales permitting calibration and reading of very fine adjustments.

volt. The electromotive force required to move one ampere across a resistance of one ohm.

watt. A measure of electrical power. One watt equals one ampere times one volt.

zenith. That point of the celestial sphere vertically overhead.

Bibliography

Baddeley, Jon, *Nautical Antiques and Collectables,* Sotheby''s Publications, London, 1993

Bames-Svamey, Patricia, *The New York Public Library Science Desk Reference,* Macmillan, New York, 1995

Barlow, Ronald S., *The Antique Tool Collector's Guide to Value,* L-W Book Sales, Gas City, Indiana, 2004

Bauer, Bruce, *The Sextant Handbook,* McGraw Hill, Inc., New York, 1995

Bays, Carter, *The Encyclopedia of Early American Sewing Machines,* Carter Bays, Columbia, SC, 1993

Bedini, Silvio A., *Early American Scientific Instruments and Their Makers,* Smithsonian Institution, Washington, 1964

Benjamin, Park, *Appletons' Cyclopedia of Applied Mechanics,* D. Appleton and Company, New York, 1895

Bierce, Ambrose, *The Devil's Dictionary,* Dover Publications, Inc., New York, 1993

Block, Arthur, *Murphy's Law and Other Reasons Why Things Go Wrong, Price/Stern/Sloan,* Los Angeles, 1984

Block, Arthur, *Murphy's Law Book Two, Price/Stern/Sloan,* Los Angeles, 1983

Block, Arthur, *Murphy's Law Book Three, Price/Stern/Sloan,* Los Angeles, 1982

Bowditch, Nathaniel, *American Practical Navigator,* U.S. Navy Hydrographic Office, Washington, 1958

Brewer, E. Cobham, *Brewer's Dictionary of Phrase and Fable*, Harper & Row, New York, 1970

Britannica Encyclopedia, 9th, 10th and 11th Editions, 1888, 1902 and 1910 respectively

Britt, Kenneth W., *Handbook of Pulp and Paper Technology,* Van Nostrand Reinhold Company, New York, 1970

Burke, James, *Connections,* Little, Brown and Company, Boston, 1978

Cardwell, Donald, *The Norton History of Technology,* W.W. Norton & Company, New York, 1994

Carpenter, William B., *The Microscope and its Revelations,* P. Blakiston's Son & Co., Philadelphia, 1901

Case Steam Engine Manual, J.I. Case Company, Racine, Wisconsin

Clay, R.S. and T.H. Court, *The History of the Microscope,* The Holland Press, London, 1975

Giedion, Siegfried, *Mechanization Takes Command,* W.W. Norton & Company, New York, 1948

Glutton, Cecil and George Daniels, *Watches,* The Viking Press, Inc., New York, 1965

Durham, Bill, *Steamboats and Modern Steam Launches,* Boat House, Portland, Oregon, 1997

Elements of Mechanical Engineering, The Colliery Engineer Co., Scranton, Pennsylvania, 1897

Elements of Surveying, TM 5-232, Department of the Army, Washington, 1953

Green, Robert E., *Machinery's Handbook, 25th Ed.,* Industrial Press, New York, 1996

Hawkins, N., *Indicator Catechism,* Theo. Audel & Co., New York, 1903

Hendrickson, Robert, *Word and Phrase Origins,* Checkmark Books, New York, 2001

Homans, James E., *Self-Propelled Vehicles,* Theo Audel & Company, New York, 1905

Hutton, F.R., *Illustrated Machine Tools of 1885,* Lindsay Publications, Manteno, IL, 1981

James W. Queen & Co. Catalogue, Philadelphia, 1880

Knight, Austin M., *Modern Seamanship,* D. Van Nostrand Company, New York, 1953

Macdonald-Taylor, Margaret, *A Dictionary of Marks,* Hawthorn Books, New York, 1962

Green, Robert E., *Machinery's Handbook,* Industrial Press, Inc., New York, 1996

McGrath, Kimberley A., *World of Invention,* Gale, Detroit, 1999

Moskowitz, Saul, *Historical Technology,* Historical Technology, Inc., Marblehead, MA, 1977-1980

Moxiey, Christina Fry, *The Official Museum Directory,* National Register Publishing, 1998

Muir, Frank, *An Irreverent and Thoroughly Incomplete Social History of Almost Everything,* Dorset Press, New York, 1976

Norfolk, Elizabeth, *Miller's International Antiques Price Guide,* Reed Consumer Books, Ltd., New York 1990-1999

Partridge, Michael, *Farm Tools,* New York Graphic Society, Boston, 1973

Payton, Crystal, *Scientific Collectibles Identification & Price Guide,* Crystal Payton, 1978

Pearsall, Ronald, *Collecting Mechanical Antiques,* Arco Publishing Company, Inc., New York, 1973

Pearsall, Ronald, *Collecting and Restoring Scientific Instruments,* Arco Publishing Company, Inc., New York, 1974

Randier, Jean, *Nautical Antiques for the Collector,* Doubleday & Company, Inc., Garden City, New York, 1977

Sande, Theodore Anton, *Industrial Archeology,* The Steven Greene Press, Brattleboro, Vt.

Schaefer,Herwin, *Nineteenth Century Modern,* Praeger Publishers, New York, 1970

Scientific American, Munn & Co., New York, 1853, 1868

Sheret, Robin, *Smoke Ash and Steam,* Western Isles Cruise and Dive Co. Ltd., Victoria, B.C., 1997

Singer, Charles, *A History of Technology,* Oxford University Press, Oxford, England, 1958

Smart, Charles E., *The Makers of Surveying Instruments in America Since 1700,* Charles E, Smart, 1962

The Engineer and Steam Engineering, The Engineer Publishing. Co., Chicago, 1904, 1905

Travers, Bridget, *World of Invention,* Gale Research , Inc., Detroit, 1994

Turner, Gerard L'e., *Collecting Microscopes,* Mayflower Books, New York, 1981

Turner, Gerard L'e., *Scientific Instruments 1500 - 1900,* University of California Press, Berkeley, 1998

Von Basserman-Jordan, Ernst, *The Book of Old Clocks and Watches,* Crown Publishers, Inc., New York, 1964

Watkins, George, *The Stationary Steam Engine,* David & Charles, Newton Abbot, Devon, 1968

Wendel, C.H., *Encyclopedia of Antique Tools & Machinery,* Krause Publications, Iola, WI., 2001

Wheatland, David P., *The Apparatus of Science at Harvard 1765 - 1800,* Harvard University, 1968

Wynter, Harriet, and Anthony Turner, *Scientific Instruments,* Charles Scribner's Sons, New York, 1975

Graphics Credits

Caboose images   Ken Houghton Rail Images and www.rrhistorical.com
Centrifuge advertisement   Cornish, Curtis & Greene Mfg. Co.
Cirker, Blanche, *3200 Old Time Cuts and Ornaments,* Dover Publications, Inc., Mineola, NY, 2001
Famous Americans, Dover Publications, Inc., Mineola, New York, 2005
Grafton, Carol Belanger, *Victorian Spot Illustrations, Alphabets & Ornaments,*
   Dover Publications, Inc., New York, 1982
Hart, Harold H., *Trades & Professions*, Hart Publishing Company, New York, 1977
Hech, J.G., *The Complete Encyclopedia of Illustration,* Park Lane, New York, 1979
Hornung, Clarence P., *Handbook of Early Advertising Art,* Dover Publications, Inc., New York, 1956
Mendenhall, John, *Scan This Book,* Art Direction Book Company, Glenbrook, CT, 1997
Mendenhall, John, *Scan This Book Two,* Art Direction Book Company, Glenbrook, CT, 1996
Mendenhall, John, *Scan This Book Three,* Art Direction Book Company, Glenbrook, CT, 1998
Storey, Daniel E., Photograph of hat block

Index

Abbé, Ernst 15
Abney level 131
acetylene 63
achromatic lens 36
acquisition 183
Adam and Eve 14, 144
Adams, Sr., George 135
admiralty arrow 29
aerial surveys 140
African Queen 52
air whistle, caboose 170
Ajax Engineering Co. 38
Albert Pick & Co. 9
alcohol 107
alembec 107
alidade 125, 139
alternating current 69
altitude 110
amber 68
American Steam Gauge & Valve Mfg. Co. 57
ammeter, alternating current 69
ammeter, direcrt current 67, 68
ampere 67, 203
Ampère, André-Marie 67, 68
Amsler, Jacob 102, 126
anchors 47
anemometer 100
angle-of-heel indicator 35
angle of repose 134
aneroid barometer 110
annealing 203
antique technology
    appraisal 185
    as art 182
     collectors associations 202
    value 185
apothecaries weights 169
apple peeler 14
Arcade Manufacturing 7
Archimedes 108
arc light 77
arcograph 102
Aristotle 11, 152
Ashcroft, Edward 56, 59
Ashton Valve Co. 56
Atlantic cable 53, 71
Awdrey, William Vere 51
azimuth 31, 46, 128, 129
Bacon, Francis 36
balance
    analytical 109
    steelyard 174
    torsion 169
barley 172
barograph 110
barometer
    aneroid 110
    Fortin 118
    wheel 11
Barr, Archibald 15
bathythermograph 39
beam compass 95
bearing 203
beer tap 172
Belshazzar 169

Benny, Jack 151
B.F. Perkins & Son 93
bevel gear casting pattern 92
Bierce, Ambrose 94
binnicle 47
binoculars 15
binocular microscope 118
bitstock 143
Black & Decker 74
blasting machine 81
Bligh, William 27
block 41, 47
blowtorch 154
boatswain's pipe 46
boring machine 156
bort 176
boiler water gauge 63
bottle frame engine 62
Bourdon, Eugene 56, 110
Bounty 27
box sextant 29
boxwood 146
Brady, James Buchanan 56
Brahe, Tycho 125
brakeman 170
Bramah, Joseph 16
Brancusi 182
Breuget 182
brewer 172
Brown, John 124
Brunel, Isambard Kingdom 41
Brunel, Marc Isambard 41
Buff & Buff Manufacturing Company 99
buggy whip 179
Burgess, Gelett 165
butter fat 165
caboose 170
CAD 94, 95, 104, 140, 153
calcium carbide 163
calculating machine 88, 102
calipers 147
caliper testing gauge 103
cam 94, 203
CAM 104, 153
camera 161
Capek, Karl 158
Caporael, Linnda R. 164
carbide lamp 163
carbon arc lamp 77
Carlisle & Finch Co. 77
Cauchoix, Robert-Aglae 98
celestial globe 30
celestial navigation 3
centrifuge 165
CERN 120
Chicago Hardware Foundry Co. 14
Chihuly, Dale 45
Chronik, Brothers 177
Churchill, Winston 43
Clayton & Lambert Mfg. Co. 154
cleaning 195
clinometer 134,139
clock 10
Coates, Moses 14
coffee grinder 7

Coit, Lillie 68
Cole, Humphrey 129
collecting 181
collimation 203
Columbus, Christopher 48
combination tool 157
compass
    navigational 31
    rose 31
    surveying 124
Comptometer 88
computers 82, 84
computer assisted design 94, 104
computer aided engineering 104
computer aided machining 104
concrete 111
condition 186
Conn, C.G. 32
conservation 195
corner brace, 157
counterpoise 174
Cook, James 27
Cooke, William 72
cork puller 23
Cornish, Curtis & Greene Mfg. Co. 165
correcting dip needle 32
Coulomb, Charles 67, 119
crank 143
cream separator 63
Crookes tube 116
Crookes railway tube 118
Crookes, William 116
crosscut saw 62
cytometer 120
Daedalus 85
dairyman 165
Dallmeyer, J.H. 161
dates of invention for
    devices and fasteners 190
    materials 190
    processes 190
dating technology 189
Davenport, Thomas 73
Da Vinci, Leonardo 85
Davis, Leonard L. 149
Davy, Humphry 83, 162
deadeye 40
De Laval, Carl Gustaf 63
dendrochronologist 112
design 189
De Vilbiss Company, The 150
diamond 176
Detroit Lubricator Co. 55
Dietzgen, Eugene 123
Dietzgen, Joseph 123
dip needle 32, 136
direct current 67
diving hood 44
DNA 68
dough 173
drafting set 94
Draper, Daniel 101
drill 143, 156
duck press 9
dumpy level 127, 128
dynamo 83
dynamometer 102, 103

EASCO 43
Edison, Thomas 69, 85
EDM 140
Einstein, Albert 10, 72
electric drill 74
electric fan 82
electric light bulb 82
electric motor 73, 82
electric razor 80
electrometer 119
electronic distance measurement 132
electrostatic generator 83
elektron 68
ellipsograph 95
engine turning 18
ergot 164
Ericsson, John 42
Everest, George 129
Exxon Valdez 25
Fahrenheit, Daniel 96
fakes 192
fan 82
Faraday, Michael 76
Felt & Tarrant Mfg. Co. 88
fettle 92
Fidelity Electric Company 81
fire damp 162
fire hose nozzle 168
Fiske, Bradley Allen 38
flash point tester 115
fluter 23
Frankenstein 65, 67
fishnet floats 45
focal length 203
flotsam 45
folding rule 146
Ford, Henry 150
forgeries 192
Fortin barometer 118
fractal 60
Fowler, L.N. 117
Franklin, Benjamin 65, 100, 172
Fresnel, Augustin 37
Fuller, George 87
function 189
Galileo 10, 36, 152
Galvani, Luigi 70
Gambrinus 172
Gascoigne, William
gasket cutter 60
gear 92
General Electric Corporation 67, 69, 97
George, Donny 176
Gilbert, William 68
Gilgamesh 172
glass cutter 176
global positioning system 48, 140
Goldberg, Rube 85
Gould, Jay 170
governor, steam 54, 63
grain probe 164
Grant, Ulysses S. 89
Great Eastern 53
Gunter's chain, 132
Gunter, Edmund 103, 132
Gurley, W. & L. E. 134
Halley, Edmund 28

Hammond Multiplex 167
Hampden Watch Co. 18
Hammer, Armand 18
hand drill 156
harmonica, player 17
harmonograph 118
Heath & Co. 27
Heele 114
Helios 114, 171
helium 114
Henry, B. Tyler
Herbert & Sons, Ltd. 174
Hercules 13
Hercules Powder Co. 81
Hobbs, A.G 16
Hollereith, Herman 82
Holtzer-Cabot Electric Co. 76
hops 172
horizon glass 27, 203
horsepower, indicated 52
Howe, Elias 12
Hubble space telescope 120
Huddart, Joseph 137
Humley, H.L. 104
Huygens, Christian 10
hydrometer 108
hygrometer 119
ice cream freezer 28
ILS 79
inclination compass 32
incremental core sampler 112
industrial revolution 21
infra red 116
injector, water 62
integrated circuit 84
interchangeable parts 21
international morse code 72
internet 187
Janssen, Pierre 114
jetsam 45
jewels 175
job descriptions 159
job stick 178
John Lilley & Son 129
Jones, William 29
Kelvin 96
Kettering, Charles 87
Keuffel & Esser Co. 13, 100, 123, 126,
        127, 130, 131, 137
Kilby, Jack 84
Kircher, Athanasius 75
Klay, A.K. 51
Knight, Austin 43
Knight, Margret E. 93
knots 34
LaCombe, Jean 29
Lady Be Good 79
Laflin & Rand Powder Co. 81
lagan 45
Lake, John C. 8
lamp target 138
lanterns 46
laser 140
lathe 141, 175
latitude 27, 203
LaTour D'Argent 9
Lavosier, Antoine 109

Leeds, Morris Evans 78
Leiberkühn 113
lemon squeezer 22
letter copying press 166
level 138
        Abney 131
        dumpy 128
        hand 130
        wye 127
leveling rod 139
Lewis and Clark 123
light bulb 82
lightening rod 65
Lilley & Son 129
limelight 77
Lincoln, Abraham 121
line shaft 73, 89
Lippershey, Hans 36
Lissajous, Jules Antoine
lock 16
Locke, John 130
locomotive 64
Loftus, William Robert 108
log 34
logarithms 87
longitude 27, 203
L.S. Starrett Co. 95
lubricant tester 103
Lufkin 146
Lusitania 64
machinists' level 149
magic lantern 75
magnetic declination 32
magneto 76
maker's marks 193
manometer 63
man overboard marker light 43
manufacturing methods and
        materials 190
marine searchlight 77
Marlin, John Mahlon 21
marlin spike 46
Marx, Karl 123
mass production 21
masthead light 37
mathematical solids 102
Mather, Cotton 164
Matthew Walker knot 40
Maudsley, Henry 147
Mauretania 64
mercury 96, 110
micrometer 147
microscope 113
milk testing centrifuge 165
miller 99
Miller-Dunn Co. 44
milling 203
miner 162, 163
mining dip needle 136
miter box 156
Monash, John 166
Monitor Sad Iron Co. 8
Moore, Gordon 84
Morse, Samuel 72
mortise scribing gauge 144
Mullen tester 93
Murdoch, William 53

Nachet, Camille Sebastian 113
Napier, John 87
National Sewing Machine Co. 12
navigation 25
Nebuchadnezar 78
Newton, Isaac 106
Niijima floats 45
Ninkasi 172
Northrup, Edwin F. 78
Novelty Iron Works 7
Noyce, Robert 84
Oakley, Annie 21
Oberhäuser, George 113
objective 203
Occan's Razor 80
occupational titles 159
OCLE 52
octant 28
ocular 203
odometer 138
Oersted's apparatus 118
Ohio Tool Co. 145
ohm 203
Ohm, Georg Simon 67
optical square 135
orrery 119
oscillating steam engine 53
paddlewheel 53
paint spray gun 150
pantograph 102
paper tester 93
parallel ruler 53
Pascal, Blaise 110
patent numbers, dates of 191
Patton, George 140
pelorus 47
Perdicaris Incident 71
Peress, Joseph 44
Perfection Magneto Co., The 76
Périer, Florin 110
pharmacist 169
phrenological bust 117
phonograph 23
photographic exposure time 23
Pickering Governor Co. 54
Pisa, leaning tower of 152
pitch ratio 42
plane, plow 145
plane table 125, 138
planetarium 119
planimeter 102, 126
planishing 203
Plath, Carl 35
plumb bob 152
pocket surveying compass 123
pocket watch 18
poise 174
polariscope 119
polymerization 203
potato peeler 23
Powell & Lealand 182
Precision Thermometer &
    Instrument Co. 96
propeller, airplane 91
propeller, marine 42, 46
protractor 137, 148
pulley, belt 89
pump 22

Pygmalion 153
Pythagorus 135
Q.R.S. DeVry Corp. 17
radar 38
radiometer 116
radio naviugation indicator 79
Ramsey, William 114
Rankine 96
refraction 36, 203
refractometer 119
reproductions 192
research 187
restoration 195
reused artifacts 197
Revere, Paul 124
revolution counter 58,63
Rice, Edwin W. 67
rifle 21
Rittenhouse, Benjamin 121
Rivers, Joan 5
robots 141, 158
Roe, Justus 133
Roebling, Augustus 85
roller organ 22
roughness 97
rye 164
sad iron 8
safety lamp, miner's 162
safety valve, pop 57
sausage stuffer 22 saw gauge 156
scanning tunneling microscope 120
Schick, Jacob 80
sciopticon 75
screw propeller 42
scrivener 166
scruple 169
SCUBA 44
sculpting tools, pattern makers 153
searchlight, marine 77
self-recording thermometer 101
sewing machine 12
sextant 27
    box 29
Shaw, George Bernard 80
Shelly, Mary 65
ship's block 41
Shaler, Saul 80
ship's telegraph 46
Siebe, Augustus 44
Siemans, Ernst 83
sieve 111
sight feed lubricator 55
Signal Electric Co. 72
Sikes hydrometer 108
Singer, Isaac Merritt 12
slide projector 75
slide rule, cylindrical 87
solar transit 138
solenoid 203
Sonar 39, 47
sounding machine 47
sources 184
specific gravity 108
spectroscope 114
speed cone 89
speed indicator 90
spherical aberration 36
spherometer 98

Spilhaus, Athelstan 39
spinning jenny 13
spinning wheel 13
Spinoza, Baruch 37
spline 103, 204
sprue hole 204
spyglass 36
stadimeter 38
Stanley Co. 146
Stanley, William Ford 29, 128
star finder 30
star globe 30
Starrett, L.S. 90, 148
station pointer 137
steam engine
    horizontal 51
    indicator 59
    marine 52
    oscillating cylinder 53
    pressure 56, 62
steam pressure gauge 56, 62
steam saw 62
steam whistle 61
steelyard 174
Stradivari, Antonio 151
Stroud, William 15
Sultana 57
surveying 121
surveying tape 133
surveyor's compass 123, 124
surveyor's chain 132
surveyor's cross 139
Swift, Jonathan 88
tabulating machine 82
tachometer 90
taffrail log register 34
Tagliabue, Giuseppe 115
tea kettle 19
technology 198
technology as art 182
telegraph key 72
telescope 36
temperature potentiometer 78
Tesla, Nikola 69
testing sieves 111
testing set 71
Thaxter, Samuel 28
Thimonier, Barthelemy 12
theodolite 129
thermocouple 78
thermometer
    dough 173
    industrial 96
    self-recording 101
Thompson, Elihu 67, 69
thread counter 177
tobacco cutter 23
tolerance 146
Torricelli, Evangelista 11
Torsion Balance Co. 169

total station 140
trammel points 95
traveler 171
traverse line 204
trunion 53, 204
tufting tool 155
turbine 63, 64, 91
Twain, Mark 178
typewriter 167
universal bevel protractor 148
universal plane 157
vacuum 11, 119
vacuum pump 119
valuation 185
Varley, C.F. 71
vernier 129, 204
Vidie, Lucien 110
violin molds 151
volt 204
Volta, Alessandro 70
voltmeter 70
VOR 79
wallpaper printing cylinder 20
Washington, George 121
watchmaker's lathe 175
water current meter 99
Waterhouse, Keith 65
water wheel 99
watt 53, 204
Watt, James 53, 85
W.D. Allen Mfg. Co. 168
weather station 23
weighman 174
Weil, Kurt 30
Welch, W.M., Mfg. Co. 124
Welles, Orson 31
Wells, H.G. 31
West, Mae 128
Weston, Edward 70
Wheatstone, Charles 72
wheel barometer 11
wheelwright 171
whistle
    air 170
    bell 61
    organ 61
    steam 61
White, April 177
Whitney Electrical Instrument Co 68.
Whitney, Eli 21
Whitman, Walt 117
Whitworth, Joseph 147
Wilcox & Gibbs 12
witch 164
Wimhurst, James 83
Wolf Safety Lamp Co. 162
wrench 156
Wright, Wilbur and Orville 85, 91, 100
wye level 127
zenith 204
zero tolerance 147